If you would like to know how t
in Speech and Communication, j
0171 382 7167 (tel) or 0171 38

SPEAK THE WORDS

ANTHOLOGY OF POETRY, PROSE AND PLAY-SCENES

Editorial Director: Eric Hollis

Managing Editor: Catriona McKay-Haynes

The editor wishes to acknowledge the valuable contribution that was made to the development of this publication by Susan Ford, Mary Greenslade, Rosemary Hoggett and other examiners.

Examinations Service
Guildhall School of Music and Drama
Barbican, London EC2Y 8DT. Tel: 0171 382 7167

GUILDHALL
SCHOOL
of
Music
&
Drama

EXAMINATIONS
SERVICE

IN THE BARBICAN
LONDON

Foreword

This is an anthology for speaking and listening, rather than for silent reading. When we lift up our voices and speak words, we put them out into the world. The words we utter are perhaps the most powerful means of communication that we have as human beings. We should all, whether children or adults, learn to use the power of the spoken word, and use it to good purpose.

Those of us whose first language is English are fortunate to have a rich resource available to us. The English language has a huge and expressive vocabulary. Yet often we barely skim its surface. Writers can make us more aware of its richness, of its capacity to describe the world, to evoke images and to express ideas. They can extend our awareness of that world, those images and ideas. They can help us to communicate our own knowledge and understanding and to hear other people's.

This is the twenty-second GSMD anthology. Its aim is the same as the first – to foster a love of literature and the spoken word. It contains poems, prose and play scenes which have been added for the GSMD Grade examinations in Speech and Drama, 1996 to 98. (Selections for the examinations may also be taken from the 21st Anthology.) But it can be used by all teachers and students, whether or not they wish to enter the examinations. The pieces are arranged under each Grade, so that they provide a possible progression from simple language suitable for young or inexperienced speakers, to more complex language requiring greater maturity and vocal facility. The progression is only a guideline. Everyone will find pieces that stimulate them. So browse through the book, read bits aloud, experience the sound and the meaning of the words and phrases, both by speaking them and by listening.

Teachers who have not made use of the GSMD Examinations Service may feel encouraged to enter candidates for the first time. The experience of working to a goal can be stimulating for students, and the feedback from an examiner will often be illuminating and constructive for both students and teachers. Modern teachers are often required to encourage and assess 'oracy' when they do not have the necessary knowledge and skill to do so. The support of GSMD can be of great help here. All our examiners are themselves skilled and experienced teachers eager to pass on what they have learnt. At the same time, GSMD would like feedback from teachers on how they have used the anthology and/or the Examinations Service, and any suggestions for the future.

Dr. Diana Devlin
Head of Drama Studies

Contents

Junior Preliminary

Brian Patten
The Frogologist

>I hate it when grown-ups say,
>'What do you want to be?'
>I hate the way they stand up there
>And talk down to me.
>
>I say:
>
>'I want to be a frogologist
>And study the lives of frogs,
>I want to know their habitat
>And crawl about in bogs,
>I want to learn to croak and jump
>And catch flies with my tongue
>And will they please excuse me 'cause
>Frogologists start quite young.'

Judith Nicholls
The Dentist

>I love to visit my dentist
>and read the comics there,
>to see his rows of clackety teeth
>and ride in his moving chair.
>
>I love to visit my dentist
>and stare at his stripy fish,
>to see the pink fizz in the glass
>and the fillings on the dish.
>
>I love to visit my dentist
>and see his tools all gleam,
>but when I need a filling –
>well, then I'm not so keen!

Charles Causley
Spin Me a Web, Spider

Spin me a web, spider,
Across the window-pane
For I shall never break it
And make you start again.

Cast your net of silver
As soon as it is spun,
And hang it with the morning dew
That glitters in the sun.

It's strung with pearls and diamonds,
The finest ever seen,
Fit for any royal King
Or any royal Queen.

Would you, could you, bring it down
In the dust to lie?
Any day of the week, my dear,
Said the nimble fly.

Wes Magee
Pebble-Eye Jones (from Four Pirates)

Captain Jones of the 'Golden Locket'
lost an eye while off Cape Crockett,
stuffed a pebble in the socket.

Liked his prisoners to walk the plank
and giggled as they fell… and sank.
Grew fat and rich – a walking bank.

Max Fatchen
Why is it?

> *Why is it,*
> That,
> In our bathroom,
> It's not the dirtiest
> Or the strongest
> Who stays longest?
> BUT
> It always seems to be
> The one who gets there
> Just ahead
> Of me.
>
> Why is it
> That people fret
> When they're wet,
> With loud cries
> And soap in their eyes
> And agonized howls,
> Because they forget
> Their towels?
>
> Why is it that –
> When *I'm* in the bath,
> Steaming and dreaming,
> My toes just showing
> And the hot water flowing,
> That other people
> Yell and say,
> 'Are you there to stay
> Or just on a visit?'
>
> Why is it?

Michael Morpurgo and Shoo Rayner

from **Martians at Mudpuddle Farm** *(Chapter One)*

There was once a family of all sorts of animals that lived in the farmyard behind the tumble-down barn on Mudpuddle Farm.

At first light every morning Frederick, the flame-feathered cockerel, lifted his eyes to the sun and crowed and crowed until the light came on in old Farmer Rafferty's bedroom window.

One by one the animals crept out into the dawn and stretched and yawned
and scratched themselves.

But no one ever spoke a word – not until after breakfast.

Catherine Sefton

Beware of the Ghost! *(from The Ghost and Bertie Boggin, Chapter One)*

'You'll be my friend, won't you?' said Bertie anxiously.

'Oh yes, of course I will,' said the Ghost. 'It is a long time since I had someone to be friends with.'

'Good,' said Bertie. 'We'll be Best Friends, won't we?'

'Best Friends,' said the Ghost. 'Yes. I like the sound of that. We'll be Best Friends, Bertie.'

Bertie went to sleep, and the Ghost curled up on the mantelpiece and lay there glowing softly until midnight came, when it was time to put on his coat and go out haunting again.

Preliminary

Theresa Heine
The Lonely Dragon

A dragon is sad
Because everyone thinks
A dragon is fierce and brave,
And roars out flames,
And eats everybody,
Whoever comes near his cave.
But a dragon likes people,
A dragon needs friends,
A dragon is lonely and sad,
If anyone knows
Of a friend for a dragon,
A dragon would be very glad.

Shel Silverstein
The Silver Fish

While fishing in the blue lagoon,
I caught a lovely silver fish,
And he spoke to me, 'My boy,' quoth he,
'Please set me free and I'll grant your wish:
A kingdom of wisdom? A palace of gold?
Or all the fancies your mind can hold?'
And I said, 'OK', and I set him free,
But he laughed at me as he swam away,
And left me whispering my wish
Into a silent sea.

Today I caught that fish again
(That lovely silver prince of fishes),
And once again he offered me,
If I would only set him free,

Any one of a number of wishes
If I would throw him back to the fishes.

He was delicious.

Julie Holder
Nothing

He thought he heard
A footstep on the stair,
'It's nothing,' he said to himself,
'Nothing is there.'
He thought then he heard
A snuffling in the hall,
'It's nothing,' he said again,
'Nothing at all.'
But he didn't open the door
In case he found nothing
Standing there,
On foot or tentacle or paw.
Timidly quiet he kept to his seat
While nothing stalked the house
On great big feet.
It was strange though
And he'd noticed this
When on his own before,
Nothing stalked throughout the house
But never through his door.
The answer he thought,
Was very plain. It was because there was nothing there –
Again!

Max Fatchen
Hair

I despair
About hair
  With all the fuss
  For us
Of snipping
And clipping,
  Of curling
  And twirling,
Of tying
And drying,
  And lopping
  And flopping,
And flurries
And worries,
  About strength
  The length,
As it nears
The ears
  Or shoulder.
  When you're older
It turns grey
Or goes away
  Or leaves a fuzz
  Hair does!

Judith Nicholls
Counting Sheep

Longhorn
shorthorn
fluffy-tail
ewe

woollyhead
furry-leg
Derby ram too…
Woolly sweater
woolly socks
this is how they grew!
Snip it, clip it,
spin it, knit it…
just
    for
        YOU!

Joyce Dunbar

Stuff (from *Mouse and Mole*)

'Help!' cried Mole the next morning. 'I am being buried alive.' 'I know just how you feel,' said Mouse. 'Come on. We will have to tidy up.'

'But we tidied up yesterday,' said Mole.

'We did. But we did it all wrong,' said Mouse. 'The problem you see, is stuff. We've got too much stuff. We didn't tidy it up at all. We moved it from room to room. We need to get rid of it altogether.'

'But I like stuff,' said Mole. 'Stuff is very interesting. It might come in useful one day.'

'You can have stuff, or you can have space,' said Mouse. 'But you can't have both.'

'But what is the use of space if you have no stuff to put in it?' asked Mole.

'Space is space,' said Mouse, 'and stuff is stuff. Come on. Let's take some stuff to the rubbish dump and we can have some space for a change. Help me to fill these sacks.'

Together they filled three sacks.

'You are right, Mouse,' said Mole when they had finished.

'Look at all this lovely space. No more tidying up! No more stuff to tidy!'

David McKee

Not now, Bernard

'Hello, Dad,' said Bernard.

'Not now, Bernard,' said his father.

'Hello, Mum,' said Bernard.

'Not now, Bernard,' said his mother.

'There's a monster in the garden and it's going to eat me,'
said Bernard.

'Not now, Bernard,' said his mother.

Bernard went into the garden.

'Hello, Monster,' he said to the monster.

The monster ate Bernard up, every bit.

Then the monster went indoors.

'ROAR,' went the monster behind Bernard's mother.

'Not now, Bernard,' said Bernard's mother.

The monster bit Bernard's father.

'Not now, Bernard,' said Bernard's father.

'Your dinner's ready,' said Bernard's mother.

She put the dinner in front of the television.

The monster ate the dinner.

Then it watched the television.

Then it read one of Bernard's comics.

And broke one of his toys.

'Go to bed. I've taken up your milk,' called Bernard's mother.

The monster went upstairs.

'But I'm a monster,' said the monster.

'Not now, Bernard,' said Bernard's mother.

Grade 1

Alfred Noyes

Daddy Fell into the Pond

Everyone grumbled. The sky was grey.
We had nothing to do and nothing to say.
We were nearing the end of a dismal day.
And there seemed to be nothing beyond.
   Then
      Daddy fell into the pond!

And everyone's face grew merry and bright,
And Timothy danced for sheer delight.
'Give me the camera, quick, oh quick!
He's crawling out of the duckweed! Click!

Then the gardener suddenly slapped his knee,
And doubled up, shaking silently,
And the ducks all quacked as if they were daft,
And it sounded as if the old drake laughed.
Oh, there wasn't a thing that didn't respond
   When
      Daddy fell into the pond!

Pie Corbett

Wind Poem

Wind slices its icy blade.

Wind raids trees,
smacks leaves up back streets.

Wind somersaults sheets,
bustles and kicks.

Wind flexes muscles,
flicks its quivering wrist.

Wind twists dustbins
into clattering cartwheels.

Wind curls its steel tongue
like a shout flung at the sky.

Wind sighs;
Dies.

Judith Nicholls
The Bookshop

Welcome to the bookshop,
the books are yours to buy!
We've big ones, small ones, funny, sad
tales to make you cry…

but

DON'T TOUCH THE BOOKS!

We've poems, stories, sagas
to make you catch your breath…
tales of love and tales of war,
tales of life and death…

just

DON'T TOUCH THE BOOKS!

Toys and television
are both things of the past –
reading is the thing today,
reading pleasures last…

but

please

DON'T TOUCH THE BOOKS!

Vernon Scannell

Death of a Snowman

> I was awake all night,
> Big as a polar bear,
> Strong and firm and white.
> The tall black hat I wear
> Was draped with ermine fur.
> I felt so fit and well
> Till the world began to stir
> And the morning sun swell.
> I was so tired, began to yawn;
> At noon in the humming sun
> I caught a severe warm;
> My nose began to run,
> My hat grew black and fell,
> Was followed by my grey head.
> There was no funeral bell,
> But by tea-time I was dead.

Kit Wright

Granny Tom

> There's a cat among the pigeons
> In the yard, in the yard,
> And it seems he isn't trying
> Very hard.
> Should a pigeon chance to swoop,
> You can see his whiskers droop
> And his tail not twitch its loop
> In the yard.
>
> For the cat is growing old
> In the yard, in the yard,
> And the pigeons leave him cold.
> He has starred

In his youth in many chases,
When he put them through their paces.
Now he knows just what his place is
In the yard.

He's a snoozer in the sun
And his hunting days are done.
He's a dozer by the wall
And he pounces not at all
For he knows he no more can. He
Might well be the pigeons' granny
In the yard!

Clive King
from Stig of the Dump (Chapter 4)

'Quick, Stig, they're coming!' exclaimed Barney. 'Get back into our hiding place!' And he pulled Stig back into the mouth of the earth. As he did so a large fox-hound came out on to the track and lolloped towards them on the scent of the fox. It came straight for where they were hiding, looked up and saw Stig, and bared its teeth and growled.

Stig bared *his* teeth and growled.

The hound looked surprised. It wasn't sure whether Stig was animal or human, but he was certainly lying between it and a good strong scent.

Barney sat at the back of the little cave, holding his middle. The hound looked very big and fierce too, and he was afraid it might hurt Stig. But then Stig was looking very fierce too, and he might hurt the hound.

Stig was the first to move. With a lightning spring he darted forward and bit the hound hard on the ear. It was too much for the poor animal. It was not afraid of sharp-toothed foxes or other animals that fought back, but Stig smelt like a man and it had never heard of a man biting a dog. It turned and made off yelping, with its tail between its legs.

Frances Hodgson Burnett

from The Secret Garden (Chapter 13)

Mary stood near the door with her candle in her hand holding her breath. Then she crept across the room, and as she drew nearer the light attracted the boy's attention and he turned his head on his pillow and stared at her, his grey eyes opening so wide that they seemed immense.

'Who are you?' he said at last in a half-frightened whisper.

'Are you a ghost?'

'No, I am not,' Mary answered, her own whispering sounding half-frightened. 'Are you one?'

He stared and stared and stared. Mary could not help noticing what strange eyes he had. They were agate-grey and they looked too big for his face because they had black lashes all round them.

'No,' he replied, after waiting a moment or so. 'I am Colin.'

'Who is Colin?' she faltered.

'I am Colin Craven. Who are you?'

'I am Mary Lennox. Mr Craven is my uncle.'

'He is my father,' said the boy.

'Your father!' gasped Mary. 'No one ever told me he had a boy! Why didn't they?'

'Come here,' he said, still keeping his strange eyes fixed on her with an anxious expression.

She came close to the bed and he put out his hand and touched her.

Ted Hughes

The Coming of the Iron Man (from *The Iron Man, Chapter 1*)

The Iron Man came to the top of the cliff.

The wind sang through his iron fingers. His great iron head, shaped like a dustbin but as big as a bedroom, slowly turned to the right, slowly turned to the left. His iron ears turned, this way, that way. He was hearing the sea. His eyes, like headlamps, glowed white, then red, then infra-red, searching the sea. Never before had the Iron Man seen the sea.

He swayed in the strong wind that pressed against his back. He swayed forward, on the brink of the high cliff.

And his right foot, his enormous iron right foot, lifted – up, out, into space, and the Iron Man stepped forward, off the cliff, into nothingness.

CRRRRRAAAASSSSSH!

Down the cliff the Iron Man came toppling, head over heels.

CRASH!

CRASH!

CRASH!

From rock to rock, snag to snag, tumbling slowly. And as he crashed and crashed and crashed.

His iron legs fell off.

His iron arms broke off, and the hands broke off the arms.

His great iron ears fell off and his eyes fell out.

His great iron head fell off.

All the separate pieces tumbled, scattered, crashing, bumping, clanging, down on to the rocky beach far below.

A few rocks tumbled with him.

Then

Silence.

Only the sound of the sea, chewing away at the edge of the rocky beach, where the bits and pieces of the Iron Man lay scattered far and wide, silent and unmoving.

David Wood and Dave and Toni Arthur

from *The Pied Piper* (Act Two)

Lame Child

> No, mothers, your children did not die
> It's true you'll never see them more
> But they're not dead you can be sure
> Listen and I'll tell you why.
>
> We followed the Piper through the town
> Under his spell, unable to fight
> And as the river came in sight
> Like the rats, we thought we'd drown.
>
> We felt no fear, just joy and hope
> The Piper gave us his protection
> Then suddenly he changed direction
> And led us up the mountain slope.
>
> And as we reached the mountain's side
> A wondrous portal opened wide
> As if a cavern was suddenly hollowed
> And the Piper advanced, we children followed,
> The door in the mountainside shut fast
> When all were in to the very last…
>
> Except for me, for I am lame
> I couldn't keep up with the dance
> And so I lost my only chance
> And life will never be the same.

(The Townsfolk exit)

> It's dull in our town since my playmates left
> I can't forget that I'm bereft
> Of all the pleasant sights they see
> Which the Piper also promised me.

Grade 2

Eric Finney
Whoppers

'I'm having a pony for Christmas,
And a meal at a posh hotel.'
'That's nothing, I'm having a video
And two colour tellies as well.'

'My dad's having a Rolls Royce car.'
'Well, my dad's having two –
One for his window-cleaning gear
And one for mum – brand new.'

'My mum's having a baby.'
'well, my mum's having twins –
Or maybe she'll have triplets,
Or even quads or quins.'

'I'm having a sailing dinghy:
Cor, won't the neighbours go green!'
'We're having the yacht Britannia
Bought secondhand from the Queen.'

'We're off to the Costa Brava,
Dad's getting tickets quite soon.'
'I'll think of you then while we're on
Our luxury tour of the moon.'

'To tell you the truth, I've been fibbing
And boasting, I realize.'
'That's nothing: I've not been telling fibs,
But monstrous, walloping lies!'

Charles Causley

What has happened to Lulu?

What has happened to Lulu, mother?
    What has happened to Lu?
There's nothing in her bed but an old rag-doll
    And by its side a shoe.

Why is her window wide, mother,
    The curtain flapping free,
And only a circle on the dusty shelf
    Where her money-box used to be?

Why do you turn your head, mother,
    And why do the tear-drops fall?
And why do you crumple that note on the fire
    And say it is nothing at all?

I woke to voices late last night,
    I heard an engine roar.
Why do you tell me the things I heard
    Were a dream and nothing more?

I heard somebody cry, mother,
    In anger or in pain,
But now I ask you why, mother,
    You say it was a gust of rain.

Why do you wander about as though
    You don't know what to do?
What has happened to Lulu, mother?
    What has happened to Lu?

Russell Hoban
What the Wind Said

'Far away is where I've come from,' said the wind
'Guess what I've brought you.'
   'What?' I asked.
'Shadows dancing on a brown road by an old
Stone fence,' the wind said. 'Do you like that?'
   'Yes ,' I said. 'What else?'
'Daisies nodding, and the drone of one small airplane
In a sleepy sky,' the wind continued.
   'I like the airplane, and the daisies too,' I said.
   'What else!'
'That's not enough?' the wind complained.
   'No,' I said. 'I want the song that you were singing.
   Give me that.'
'That's mine,' the wind said. 'Find your own.' And left.

Leslie Norris
A Tiger in the Zoo

He stalks in his vivid stripes
The few steps of his cage,
On pads of velvet quiet,
In his quiet rage.

He should be lurking in shadow,
Sliding through long grass
Near the water hole
Where plump deer pass.

He should be snarling around houses
At the jungle's edge,
Baring his white fangs, his claws,
Terrorising the village!

But he's locked in a concrete cell,
His strength behind bars,
Stalking the length of his cage,
Ignoring visitors.

He hears the last voice at night,
The patrolling cars,
And stares with his brilliant eyes
At the brilliant stars.

Jack Prelutsky
Today is very boring

Today is very boring,
it's a very boring day,
there is nothing much to look at,
there is nothing much to say,
there's a peacock on my sneakers,
there's a penguin on my head,
there's a dormouse on my doorstep,
I am going back to bed.

Today is very boring,
it is boring through and through,
there is absolutely nothing
that I think I want to do,
I see giants riding rhinos,
and an ogre with a sword,
there's a dragon blowing smoke rings,
I am positively bored.

Today is very boring,
I can hardly help but yawn,
there's a flying saucer landing in the middle of my lawn,
a volcano just erupted
less than half a mile away,
and I think I felt an earthquake,
it's a very boring day.

Robert Louis Stevenson
Windy Nights

>Whenever the moon and stars are set,
>>Whenever the wind is high,
>All night long in the dark and wet,
>>A man goes riding by.
>Late in the night when the fires are out,
>Why does he gallop and gallop about?
>
>Whenever the trees are crying aloud,
>>And ships are tossed at sea,
>By, on the highway, low and loud,
>>By at the gallop goes he.
>By at the gallop he goes, and then
>By he comes back at the gallop again.

Judith Nicholls
Stable Song

>She lies, a stillness in the crumpled straw
>Whilst he looks softly on the child, unsure,
>And shadows waver by the stable door.
>
>The oxen stir; a moth drifts through the bare
>Outbuilding, silken Gabriel-winged, to where
>She lies, a stillness in the crumpled straw.
>
>A carpenter, his wife, both unaware
>That kings and shepherds seek them from afar
>And shadows waver by the stable door.
>
>The child sleeps on. A drowse of asses snore;
>He murmurs gently, raises eyes to her
>Who lies, a stillness in the crumpled straw.

A cockerel crows, disturbed by sudden fear
As shepherds, dark upon the hill, appear
And shadows waver by the stable door.

The hush of birth is in the midnight air
And new life hides the distant smell of myrrh;
She lies, a stillness in the crumpled straw,
And shadows waver by the stable door.

Ted Hughes

from How the Whale Became

'It's getting too big. I must pull it up and cook it.' But he left it a day.

Next day it was twelve feet long and far too big to go into any of God's pans.

God stood scratching his head and looking at it. Already it had crushed most of his carrots out of sight. If it went on growing at this rate it would soon be pushing his house over.

Suddenly, as he looked at it, it opened an eye and looked at him. God was amazed.

The eye was quite small and round. It was near the thickest end, and farthest from the root. He walked round to the other side, and there was another eye, also looking at him.

'Well!' said God. 'And how do you do?'

The round eye blinked, and the smooth glossy skin under it wrinkled slightly, as if the thing were smiling. But there was no mouth, so God wasn't sure.

Next morning God rose early and went out into his garden.

Sure enough, during the night his new black plant with eyes had doubled its length again. It had pushed down part of his fence, so that its head was sticking out into the road, one eye looking up it, and one down. Its side was pressed against the kitchen wall.

God walked round to its front and looked it in the eye.

'You are too big', he said sternly. 'Please stop growing before you push my house down.'

To his surprise, the plant opened a mouth. A long slit of a mouth, which ran back on either side under the eyes.

'I can't,' said the mouth.

God didn't know what to say. At last he said:

'Well then, can you tell me what sort of a thing you are? Do you know?'

'I,' said the thing, 'am Whale-Wort. You have heard of Egg-Plant, and Buck Wheat, and Dog-Daisy. I am Whale-Wort.'

Well, there was nothing God could do about that.

Penelope Lively

Nat and the Great Bath Climb (from *A House Inside Out, Chapter Three*)

The Chief Wood-louse looked sternly down at the assembled crowd and began to speak. 'We are gathered together today,' he said, 'to remind ourselves of the purpose of life.' He glared at the young wood-lice. 'And what is the purpose of life?' The young wood-lice, who knew they were not supposed to answer, gazed at him respectfully.

'The purpose of life is to climb up the side of the bath. That is what we are here for. That is why we were born. No one has ever succeeded. But the purpose of life is to try. Each and every one of us. Your turn has now come. Your mothers and fathers have tried before you. Some brave spirits have tried several time. All have failed.'

There was a silence. The young wood-lice gazed at the Chief Wood-louse and felt even more nervous and important. All except Nat, who was the youngest and smallest and had been in trouble most of his life for asking too many questions. Nat was thinking.

'You will make your attempts turn and turn about, starting with the eldest. Each of you will fail, but will have made a glorious attempt, you will then have your names inscribed on the Roll of Honour.'

The young wood-lice went quite pink with pride and excitement, all except Nat, who raised one of his fourteen legs. 'Please, sir,' he said, 'why do we have to climb up the side of the bath?'

There was a gasp of horror from the crowd of wood-lice. Nat's mother fainted clean away; his father bent his head in shame.

The Chief Wood-louse stared at Nat. His whiskers twitched in fury. 'WHAT DID YOU SAY?'

Nat cleared his throat and repeated, politely and clearly, 'Why do we have to climb up the side of the bath?'

The Chief Wood-louse huffed and puffed; his little black eyes bulged; he creaked with indignation. 'BECAUSE IT'S THERE!'

Grade 3

George Barker

They Call to One Another

They call to one another
    in the prisons of the sea
the mermen and mermaidens
    bound under lock and key
down in the green and salty dens
    and dungeons of the sea,
lying about in chains but
    dying to be free:
and this is why shortsighted men
    believe them not to be
for down to their dark dungeons it
    is very hard to see.

But sometimes morning fishermen
    drag up in the net
bits of bright glass or the silver comb
    of an old vanity set
or a letter rather hard to read
    because it is still wet
sent to remind us never, never
    never to forget
the mermen and mermaidens
    in the prisons of the sea
who call to one another
    when the stars of morning rise
and the stars of evening set
    for I have heard them calling
and I can hear them, yet.

Allan Ahlberg
Billy McBone

Billy McBone
Had a mind of his own,
Which he mostly kept under his hat.
The teachers all thought
That he couldn't be taught,
But Bill didn't seem to mind that.

Billy McBone
Had a mind of his own,
Which the teachers had searched for for years.
Trying test after test,
They still never guessed
It was hidden between his ears.

Billy McBone
Had a mind of his own,
Which only his friends ever saw.
When the teacher said, 'Bill,
Whereabouts is Brazil?,'
He just shuffled and stared at the floor.

Billy McBone
Had a mind of his own,
Which he kept under lock and key.
While the teachers in vain
Tried to burgle his brain,
Bill's thoughts were off wandering free.

Brian Moses
The Way is Open

I heard that the man
who played Superman
really died…

No make-believe death
this time.
No edge-of-the-seat,
come-back-next-week
death.

It came out of the radio
like a message from his enemies,
lacking only their laughter
to make me believe
I'd heard wrongly.

It hung on the air
like a warning of doom,
filled the rooms with silence
as each one present
considered the news.

No safety net now
with which to catch
America
when she lapses.

No tough guy waiting
to bring some mad man
to his knees.

The way is open
for crooks and politicians
to do as they please.

Ted Hughes
Mushrooms on the Moon

Mushrooms on the moon are delicious.
But those who eat them become birds, beasts, or fishes.
Space-fishes, space-beasts, and space-birds.
They stray out into space in shoals and flocks and herds.

At first, rapturous and excited,
But suddenly feeling space all round them and
    above and below they are affrighted.

Then goggling space-fish go fleeting in formations,
Space-beasts go trailing here and there in endless
    migrations,
Space-birds go hurtling from one end of space to
    the other in endless agitations
Among the constellations.

But space is too vast, they are lost, as if quite blind.
They are looking for the human bodies they left behind
On the tiny moon, so tiny, tiny as a dust-grain
Which they can never hope to alight on again.

Brian Patten
The Newcomer

'There's something new in the river,'
The fish said as it swam –
'It's got no scales, no fins and no gills,
And ignores the impassable dam.'

'There's something new in the trees,'
I heard a bloated thrush sing,
'It's got no beak, no claws, and no feathers,
And not even the ghost of a wing.'

'There's something new in the warren,'
Said the rabbit to the doe.
'It's got no fur, no eyes and no paws,
Yet digs deeper than we dare go.'

'There's something new in the whiteness,'
Said the snow-bright polar-bear.
'I saw its shadow on a glacier,
But it left no pawmarks there.'

Throughout the animal kingdom
The news was spreading fast –

No beak, no claws, no feather,
No scales, no fur, no gills,
It lives in the trees and the water,
In the soil and the snow and the hills,
And it kills and it kills and it kills.

Russell Hoban
Homework

Homework sits on top of Sunday, squashing Sunday flat.
Homework has the smell of Monday, homework's very fat,
Heavy books and piles of paper, answers I don't know.
Sunday evening's almost finished, now I'm going to go
Do my homework in the kitchen. Maybe just a snack,
Then I'll sit right down and start as soon as I run back
For some chocolate sandwich cookies. Then I'll really do
All that homework in a minute. First I'll see what new
Show they've got on television in the living room.
Everybody's laughing there, but misery and gloom
And a full refrigerator are where I am at.
I'll just have another sandwich. Homework's very fat.

Barbara Giles
Drought in the Mallee, 1940

> The dunes slide to swallow
> a house like a child's toy
> forgotten in sand play.
>
> Thirty miles south they're hopeful still,
> plant money each year
> burying wheat to see it shoot and die.
>
> Dry follows dry.
> 'I selected here. I rolled the Mallee,
> put the first crops in.
>
> I've grown wheat all my life.
> There'll be good years again.'
> Sand spreads from naked roadsides
>
> across sown land, all parched
> and blowing. The red dust
> reaches the city three hundred miles away.
>
> Mick's gone before good years. His sons
> breed pigs, grow barley and diversify
> and saved in the nick of time
>
> sell out and move away.

Henry Lawson
The Water-Lily

> A lonely young wife
> In her dreaming discerns
> A lily-decked pool
> With a border of ferns,
> And a beautiful child,
> With butterfly wings,

Trips down to the edge of the water and sings:
     'Come, mamma! come!
     Quick! follow me!
Step out on the leaves of the water-lily!'

     And the lonely young wife,
     Her heart beating wild,
     Cries, 'Wait till I come,
     Till I reach you, my child!'
     But the beautiful child
     With butterfly wings
Steps out on the leaves of the lily and sings:
     'Come, mamma! come!
     Quick! follow me!
And step on the leaves of the water-lily!'

     And the wife in her dreaming
     Steps out on the stream,
     But the lily leaves sink
     And she wakes from her dream
     Ah, the waking is sad,
     For the tears that it brings,
And she knows 'tis her dead baby's spirit that sings:
     'Come, mamma! come!
     Quick! follow me!
Step out on the leaves of the water-lily!'

J R R Tolkien
from The Hobbit *(Chapter 5)*

Deep down here by the dark water lived old Gollum, a small slimy
creature – as dark as darkness, except for two big round pale eyes in
his thin face. He had a little boat, and he rowed about quietly on the
lake. He paddled it with large feet dangling over the side, but never a
ripple did he make. He was looking out of his pale lamp-like eyes for
blind fish. He liked meat too. Goblin he thought good, when he could

get it; but he took care they never found him out. He just throttled them from behind, if ever they came down alone anywhere near the edge of the water, while he was prowling about.

Actually Gollum lived on a slimy island of rock in the middle of the lake. He was watching Bilbo now from the distance with his pale eyes like telescopes. Bilbo could not see him, but he was wondering a lot about Bilbo, for he could see that he was no goblin at all.

Bilbo was sitting on the brink altogether flummoxed and at the end of his way and his wits. Suddenly up came Gollum and whispered and hissed:

'Bless us and splash us, my precious! I guess it's a choice feast; at least a tasty morsel it'd make us, Gollum!' And when he said Gollum he made a horrible swallowing noise in his throat.

The hobbit jumped nearly out of his skin.

'Who are you?' He said, thrusting his dagger in front of him.

'What iss he, my preciouss?' whispered Gollum.

'I am Mr Bilbo Baggins. I have lost the dwarves and I have lost the wizard, and I don't know where I am; and I don't want to know, if only I can get away.'

'What's he got in his handses?' said Gollum, looking at the sword, which he did not quite like.

'A sword, a blade which came out of Gondolin!'

'Ssss,' said Gollum, and became quite polite. 'Praps ye sits here and chats with it a bitsy, my preciouss. It like riddles, praps it does, does it?' He was anxious to appear friendly, at any rate for the moment, and until he found out more about the sword and the hobbit, whether he was quite alone really, whether he was good to eat, and whether Gollum was really hungry.

Susan Cooper
from Seaward *(Chapter 15)*

A brightness flashed past her before she could move; it was Peth. He stood over her, leaning over the rim of the shelf of rock, eye-stalks bent down; through his spindly confusion of legs she saw the flat line of the rope, quivering. Tied to a rocky pinnacle beside her, it led to the edge over which Westerly had fallen. She crawled forward, and saw his body hanging a few feet below, limp, slowly turning.

'West!' It was a desperate shout; she knew there would be no response. But to her joyful amazement he turned his head and gave her a crooked grin.

'Stupid,' he said, croaking. 'Slipped.'

She reached for the taut rope. 'I'll pull you up.'

'No! Too hard. Catch – this.' Clutching the rope with one hand to steady himself, he groped down for the free end of line which dangled loose from his waist. Awkwardly, he flipped it up towards Cally. Twice she missed it; the edge of the shelf was slippery, and she dared not come too close. She lay flat, reaching out, and at the third attempt she caught the rope.

'Pull on that. I'll come up the other.' Westerly's voice was strained; the rope was cutting into his waist like wire, and he was giddy from the spinning sight of the huge drop below.

Cally pulled feverishly at the line, and felt him begin to rise towards the shelf. But her feet were slipping on the smooth rock; every pull took her closer to the edge. Frantically she looked round for a foothold, but could find nothing. She dropped on to her knees. 'Hang on, West!'

William Horwood

from The Willows in Winter (Chapter Ten)

Painfully, achingly, Toad pulled himself from the blackthorn hedge and looked about. Not a person, nor a horse, nor a solitary hound in sight: only his sweep's brush and bag, and the bicycle, buckled now and useless.

'I fooled them!' cried the panting, bruised and bloodied Toad. 'I put them off the scent! So near death, and yet I have escaped! Who would dare not agree that I am the greatest, cleverest Toad alive! Were the hounds of hell itself after me I would escape them! Ha! Ha!'

Thus Toad, sitting on the verge, dressed and sooted as a chimney sweep, satisfied himself that his luck was the product of his own cleverness. Then, triumphant once more, he rose unsteadily to his feet and eyed the bicycle.

'O metal steed,' said he, 'it grieves me to leave you here, for you were faithful, like no other, and you gave your life for me! I shall give you an honourable burial, and ever remember you in my prayers!'

With some difficulty, for it was heavy and every muscle and bone of his body ached, Toad took up the bicycle and portered it across the road to the ditch, into which he unceremoniously threw it, lest some busybody or other passing by should see it, and use it as evidence that he had passed that way.

As for the hunt, and what its quarry might have been, which had been of such life and death importance to Toad moments before, it mattered not one whit to him now. He had lived to tell the tale, and tell it he certainly would in the most heroic terms at the earliest opportunity. Meanwhile, he must away!

Peter Miller and Randall Lewton
from **The Sweeney Todd Shock 'n' Roll Show** *(Act One, Scene One)*

Tobias It is a long and tedious story.
Newsboy Oh well then…
(A violin plays mournfully in the background – sound effects department. The Newsboy yawns and leans against a convenient wall)

Until last week I lived a good and happy life in (local district). Since my father died when I was a baby my mother and I have lived in a simple way. We were poor but we were honest. Alas our honesty did not protect us from our evil landlord. We were thrown out to fend for ourselves in the cold, cruel world. My mother was overcome by the shame of our situation, took ill last Thursday evening – oh, I weep to think of it – she died in my arms.

Newsboy *(awaking from doze)* Yes, well… *(starts to leave)*

Tobias Before she died…

(Newsboy leans on wall again)

…she gave me this. *(produces banknote)* It was all she had, and she told me to seek an apprenticeship here in London.

Newsboy And I hope you…

Tobias For three days, an orphan, I trudged on weary feet through mud and foul weather until I reached this place. I have had nothing to eat, little to drink and my clothes are in rags. I can go no further – and I'm only little.

Newsboy You are starving, are you? You have a five pound note there. Buy yourself a dinner with that.

Tobias No! This banknote is all I have in the world. I must keep it as long as I can. If I spend this then I am doomed to poverty and starvation.

Newsboy I'd keep that money in your pocket if I were you. There are some funny characters about, you know. Well, I wish you luck mate. *(makes a quick exit)*

Tobias *(to audience)* There is more to my story than I dared to tell a stranger. *('he' removes his cap to reveal beautiful long hair)* The world is a dangerous place for a young girl, alone, without a friend or protector. This disguise has deceived all those whom I have met on my journey and now I hope it will enable me to find a home and earn a living. *(she replaces the cap tucking in her hair)* …although I must confess that I am at a loss to know where to begin my search. I am lost and weary and the wind stings through these ragged clothes. I started my journey with strength and a confident heart but now… now… I think constantly of my poor mother and my heart grows heavy. *(She sobs)*

Grade 4

Raymond Wilson

This Letter's to Say

Dear Sir or Madam,
This letter's to say
Your property
Stands bang in the way
Of Progress, and
Will be knocked down
On March the third
At half-past one.

There is no appeal,
Since the National Need
Depends on more
And still more Speed,
And this, in turn,
Dear Sir or Madam,
Depends on half England
Being tar-macadam.
(But your house will –
We are pleased to say –
Be the fastest lane
Of the Motorway).

Meanwhile the Borough
Corporation
Offer you new
Accommodation
Three miles away
On the thirteenth floor
(Flat Number Q
6824).

But please take note,
The Council regret:
No dog, cat, bird
Or other pet;
No noise permitted,
No singing in the bath
(For permits to drink
Or smoke or laugh
Apply on Form
Z327);
No children admitted
Aged under eleven;
No hawkers, tramps
Or roof-top lunchers;
No opening doors
To Bible-punchers.

Failure to pay
Your rent, when due,
Will lead to our
Evicting you.
The Council demand
That you consent
To the terms above
When you pay your rent.

Meanwhile we hope
You will feel free
To consult us
Should there prove to be
The slightest case
Of difficulty.

With kind regards.
Yours faithfully…

Roger McGough

Three Rusty Nails

Mother, there's a strange man
Waiting at the door
With a familiar sort of face
You feel you've seen before.

Says his name is Jesus
Can we spare a couple of bob
Says he's been made redundant
And now can't find a job.

Yes I think he is a foreigner
Egyptian or a Jew
Oh aye, and that reminds me
He'd like some water too.

Well shall I give him what he wants
Or send him on his way?
OK I'll give him 5p
Say that's all we've got today.

And I'll forget about the water
I suppose it's a bit unfair
But honest, he's filthy dirty
All beard and straggly hair.

Mother, he asked about the water
I said the tank had burst
Anyway I gave him the money
That seemed to quench his thirst.

He said it was little things like that
That kept him on the rails
Then he gave me his autographed picture
And these three rusty nails.

Elizabeth Jennings
The Owl's Request

> Do not be frightened of me.
> I am a night-time creature. When the earth is still,
> When trees are shadows of shadows.
> When only the moon and its attendant stars
> Enlarge the night, when the smallest sound is shrill
> And may wake you up and frighten you,
> I am about with my friendly 'Tu-whit, tu whoo'.
>
> My face is kindly but also mysterious.
> People call me wise.
> Perhaps they do so because I sometimes close my eyes
> And seem to be thinking.
> The way I think is not like yours. I need
> No thick philosopher's book;
> I can tell the truth of the world with a look
> But I do not speak about
> What I see there. Think of me then
> As the certainty in your wandering nights.
> I can soothe men
> And will snatch you out of your doubt,
> Bear you away to the stars and moon
> And to sleep and dawn. So lie
> And listen to my lullaby.

Max Fatchen
Sea Talk

> Inside the little harbour, on the tide
> That washes stones where weedy limpets cling,
> I thought I heard where sleeping rowboats ride,
> The little fishes' tiny whispering.

I thought I heard, beside the wooden pier,
The starfish heave a long and salty sigh
And murmur in the mussel's shelly ear,
Its longing for a bright and wider sky.

I thought I heard the underwater shouts
Of gleeful creatures… moans and barks and squeals,
The dolphins thrusting long and smiling snouts
And gossiping to sleek and agile seals…

The noises from the restless waves and spray
Of armoured crabs that guard their rocky spots,
The sound of white sea horses at their play
Or lobsters' prayers within their captive pots.

I wish I knew that such a thing could be –
To know the songs of moving fin and scales,
The liquid language of the living sea
And hear the gentle voices of the whales.

Ted Hughes
There Came A Day

There came a day that caught the summer.
Wrung its neck
Plucked it
And ate it.

Now what shall I do with the trees?
The day said, the day said.
Strip them bare, strip them bare.
Let's see what is really there.

And what shall I do with the sun?
The day said, the day said.
Roll him away till he's cold and small.
He'll come back rested if he comes back at all.

And what shall I do with the birds?
The day said, the day said.
The birds I've frightened, let them flit,
I'll hang out pork for the brave tomtit.

And what shall I do with the seed?
The day said, the day said.
Bury it deep, see what it's worth.
See if it can stand the earth.

What shall I do with the people?
The day said, the day said.
Stuff them with apple and blackberry pie –
They'll love me then till the day they die.

There came this day and he was autumn.
His mouth was wide
And red as a sunset.
His tail was an icicle.

Judith Wright
The Trap

'I love you,' said the child,
but the parrot with its blazing breast and wing
flaunted in the high tree, love's very beckoning,
and would not be beguiled.

Look how first innocence
darkens through shades of knowledge and desire!
– the bait, the trap, the patience! When the wire
snaps shut, his eyes' triumphant insolence!

'I loved it and it would not come to me.'
Now love is gone.
Cunning and will undo us. We must be
their prisoners, boy, and in a bitterer cage

endure their lifelong rage.
Look round you. See, the chains on everyone.

Quick, save yourself! Undo
that door and let him go.

John Arden and Margaretta D'Arcy
The Business of Good Government

*The Business of Good Government is a nativity play. The Hostess owns
'The Bethlehem Inn.'*

Hostess *(The Hostess comes forward with a broom, sweeping
busily, talking to the audience as she does so)* It's not as if they were all
paying for their rooms neither – half of 'em come here with a piece of
yellow paper – 'A Government chit, madam, it'll be charged to your
credit from the beginning of the next Revenue Period – take it to the
Town Hall'. The way my house is at the moment, you'd think *I* was
running the Town Hall. Civil Servants… Then there's the military – *they*
don't pay neither. 'Haw, haw, landlady, I want accommodation for a
corporal and thirteen men of Number Eight Detail, three nights
altogether, breakfasts and suppers, find their own dinners: but you'll
have to provide cooking facilities… oh yes, and covered storage for
the transport. See the place is clean.' Oh, I could lie down and die! To
say nothing of the rest of 'em. 'Have you got a room, please?' 'Could
you let us have a bed, missus?' 'Just a corner, just a mattress, just a bit
of straw – every house in the place is full, we've been all round the
town.' I know very well they're full. *I'm* full! No vacancies! Not any
more. I mean it. Why should I have my premises made a scapegoat for
administrative incompetence and I don't care who hears me! *(Shaking
her broom angrily at the Angel)* I am perfectly aware that the decree
has gone out from Caesar Augustus, young man. That's exactly what I
mean. All done as usual with no thought whatever for the
convenience of individuals… Where was I? Oh, yes, administrative
incompetence. There's more to it than that, you know. It's not just
incompetence – it's the downright inhumanity that makes me so
upset.

(Joseph and Mary enter)

(The Hostess half turns and points them out to the audience)

This poor girl from the north – all that long way in such terrible weather and the baby due any minute…What do they expect me to do? I haven't a room in the house. *(She turns and speaks to Mary)* What do you expect me to do, dear? I don't know whether I'm on my head or me heels – just look at the place, all chockablock and I'm run off me feet? You'll have to find somewhere else.

Bertolt Brecht *(Translated by James and Tania Stern, with W H Auden)* *from* **The Caucasian Chalk Circle** *(Scene Six)*

Grusha You want to pass the child on to her. She who is too refined even to know how to change its nappies! You don't know any more about Justice than I do, that's clear.

Adzak There's something in that. I'm an ignorant man. I haven't even a decent pair of trousers under my robe. See for yourself. With me, everything goes on food and drink. I was educated in a convent school. Come to think of it, I'll fine you ten piastres, too. For contempt of Court. What's more, you're a very silly girl to turn me against you, instead of making eyes at me and wagging your backside a bit to keep me in a good temper. Twenty piastres!

Grusha I'll tell you what I think of your justice, you drunken onion! How dare you talk to me as though you were the cracked Isaiah on the church window! When they pulled you out of your mother, it wasn't planned that you'd rap her over the knuckles for pinching a little bowl of corn from somewhere! Aren't you ashamed of yourself when you see how afraid I am of you? But you've let yourself become their servant. So that their houses are not taken away, because they've stolen them. Since when do houses belong to bed-bugs? But you're on the look-out, otherwise they couldn't drag our men into their wars. You bribe-taker!

(Azdak gets up. He begins to beam. With a little hammer he knocks on the table half-heartedly as if to get silence. But as Grusha's scolding continues, he only beats time with it.)

I've no respect for you. No more than for a thief or a murderer with a knife, who does what he wants. You can take the child away from me, a hundred against one, but I tell you one thing: for a profession like yours, they ought to choose only bloodsuckers and men who rape children. As a punishment. To make them sit in judgment over their fellow men, which is worse than swinging from the gallows.

Dylan Thomas
from Under Milk Wood

Narrator Now, woken at last by the out-of-bed-sleepy-head-Polly-put-the-kettle-on town hall bell, Lily Smalls, Mrs Beynon's treasure, comes downstairs from a dream of royalty, who all night long went larking with her full of sauce in the Milk Wood dark, and puts the kettle on the primus ring in Mrs Beynon's kitchen, and looks at herself in Mr Beynon's shaving glass over the sink, and sees:

(as Lily)

Oh there's a face!
Where you get that hair from?
Got it from an old tom cat.
Give it back then, love.
Oh, there's a perm!

Where you get that nose from Lily?
Got it from my father, silly.
You've got it on upside down!
Oh, there's a conk!

Look at your complexion!
Oh no, *you* look!
Needs a bit of make-up.
Needs a veil.
Oh there's glamour!

Where you get that smile, Lil?
Never you mind girl.
Nobody loves you.
That's what *you* think!

Who is it loves you?
Shan't tell.
Come on, Lily.
Cross your heart then?
Cross my heart.

Narrator And very softly, her lips almost touching her reflection, she breathes the name, and clouds the shaving glass.

Brian Owen

from **The Evil Eye of Gondōr** *(Act One, Scene Two)*

The Castle of Gondōr

An evil place, the Castle is dark and eerie. The Eye of Gondōr is upstage centre. Roth is standing in front of the Eye which throbs and glows and fades

Roth Well may you throb; well may you glow. You have brought me power but the illusion is frail. I fear, in my bones I fear. I don't know why but there's a shadow over me and thin, boney fingers seem to be clutching at my throat. And yet why should I fear? It's the Valley that should fear me! I am Roth! I am the Master of Gondōr ! Why should I fear? *(Quietly)* Yet I do… and I don't know why…

(Brasov enters, a strong and fearsome man, the Guardian gaoler)

Brasov My Lord Roth…

Roth What is it?

Brasov The new prisoners, the ones from the northern villages, have arrived.

Roth Have you shown them to their… accomodation?

Brasov Yes, my Lord.

Roth Good… very good. We'll keep them out of harm's way and…
perhaps learn a little more about those dogs in the forest. Brasov…
what is the latest news about the Outlaws?

Brasov Not much, my Lord. There are now above two score
hiding in the forest…

Roth Where they're safe from our power! Do you realize, Brasov
that we are threatened while they roam free? How can we have total
mastery over this Valley while there are still above twenty men who
deny our authority?

Brasov They still wear the Eye, my Lord.

Roth Yes, but how long will they continue to fear us if we cannot
get near them? No, we must find a way to lure them out into the open,
Brasov… and perhaps I know how we can do it. Go, see to our new
guests. Make sure they are… comfortable. And, Brasov…

Brasov Yes, my Lord?

Roth Don't take too long in finding out what we need to know…

Brasov No, my Lord.

(Brasov exits)

Roth New prisoners! This is not the way to power. Soon the Castle
will be full of prisoners… what then? Who will sow corn then? Who
will tend the sheep? A castle full of prisoners is a castle full of empty
bellies to feed. I am trapped! The Outlaws are growing in strength.
Two score now… what next month? Three score? All the time they are
free the people will see in them hope. I must crush that hope! But I
must crush it without destroying the Valley. Dead villagers pay no
taxes, neither do they produce any food. *(Turning to the Eye)* Oh, Eye
of Gondôr… we have work to do in this Valley. The illusion must not
fail. It must not be discovered…

Grade 4A

Patricia Beer
E.T. Phone Home

E.T. looked like my cousin
Who looked like many things wise
And wonderful: certain dreams,
Ancient jars in museums,
Fetishes with level eyes
And their native soil still on.

I was a child. I loved him
We could most peacefully play
Together. Our family
Feared the neighbours might think we
Were all balmy. He could say
Three or four words. One was 'Home'.

At thirteen he was taken
Away to an asylum.
For three days he wailed one word:
'Home, home, home… 'Nobody heard.
Then sedated he fell dumb
Leaving the air shaken.

Soon we were told he had died.
No property, clothes or last
Words came back. But a nurse said
That he always laughed out loud
When another inmate cursed.
Those who sent him there cried.

I heard this film was coming,
Fifty years later, on TV
And watched it. Now I often see
Rainbowing up a dark sky
And heavier by one boy,
My kin, a space-ship homing.

Peter Bland

A Cape Town Christ

The picture of Christ in a white shop window
was selling white bibles and prayers.
His hair was whiter than Cape Town beaches,
whiter than Table Mountain, whiter than waves
or white whales plunging to white Antarctica.
This Christ was whiter than those white wastes.

His eyes were blue, pale blue, like stones
dug out of the white mined earth
he purified with his gaze. He was shadowless.
He was day without night, love without pain.
When children ran to him dirt under their nails
turned to white dust. At his white feet

even the Black Sea paled. When the white
Christ smiled white light embalmed
smiling crowds of the pure and pale
who came to be laundered by love. But those
who looked on him and loved him not
felt darkness drain from them – and were afraid.

Phoebe Hesketh

Ward F4

There is no weather in my room,
a white cube, bare
except for a bedside chest; one chair.
The window behind my bed
looks blind on a blind wall,
but I cannot turn my head.

No sky; no sun;
one lamp with hard green shade
is my daylight

and nightlight.
(No flowers, please, nowhere
to put them but on the floor.)
I face the brown door, stare
at the black knob, waiting...

Nurses come and go
brisk, kind under crackling starch.
They give me pills, injections
with cheerful remarks about the weather.
But there is no weather in my room.

For twelve months I have not seen a tree
or a patch of grass.
I think I could walk again
if I saw grass.
I shut my eyes.
I can see more with my eyes shut –
heather, a bright stream,
the flash of a bird.

Autumn, Winter have wasted away;
today is the first day of Spring;
and nurse says the sun is shining...
My splints are off;
my limbs feel supple
and I'm running over grass
where the willow lets down her yellow hair.

Toffee-brown chestnut buds unclose
fingers soft as silver-fox.
There's movement among branches: a speckled thrush
swings and sings, frilling the needled larch
with promised green.
Blossom and cloud pile high, higher as I pass.
I am free; the grass is warm,
yielding to my feet...

The door opens and the doctor comes in
returning me to the white cube.
He talks of tests and treatment,
makes no promises.
Improvement is slow.

Visitors come and go
bringing rain on their coats
or a bunch of flowers –
only they bring the weather into my room.

Arnold Wesker
from The Kitchen (Interlude)

Paul Listen, I'll tell you something. I agree with Dimitri also; when the world is filled with kitchens you get pigs – I'll tell you. Next door to me, next door to where I live is a bus driver. Comes from Hoxton, he's my age, married and got two kids. He says good-morning to me, I ask him how he is, I give his children sweets. That's our relationship. Somehow he seems frightened to say too much, you know? God forbid I might ask him for something. So we make no demands on each other. Then one day the busmen go on strike. He's out for five weeks. Every morning I say to him 'Keep going mate, you'll win.' Every morning I give him words of encouragement; I say I understand his cause. I've got to get up earlier to get to work but I don't mind. We're neighbours. We're workers together, he's pleased. Then, one Sunday, there's a peace march. I don't believe they do much good but I go, because in this world a man's got to show he can have his say. The next morning he comes up to me and he says, now listen to this, he says 'Did you go on that peace march yesterday?' So I says Yes, I did go on that peace march yesterday. So then he turns round to me and he says, 'You know what? A bomb should have been dropped on the lot of them! It's a pity,' he says, 'that they had children with them cos a bomb should've been dropped on the lot!' And you know what was upsetting him? The march was holding up the traffic, the buses couldn't move so fast! Now

I don't want him to say I'm right, I don't want him to agree with what I did, but what terrifies me is that he didn't stop to think that this man helped me in my cause so maybe, only *maybe*, there's something in his cause.

Joan Littlewood
from Oh What a Lovely War (Act Two)

(ENGLAND – during the First World War)

(Mrs Pankhurst is making an anti-war speech amidst much heckling)

Mrs Pankhurst Now, before talking to you all, I should like to read you a letter from my friend George Bernard Shaw. He says: 'the men of this country are being sacrificed to the blunders of boobies, the cupidity of capitalists, the ambition of conquerors, the lusts and lies and rancours of bloodthirsts that love war, because it opens their prison doors and sets them on the throne of power and popularity.'

For the second time peace is being offered to the sorely tried people of the civilised world. At the close of 1915 President Wilson proposed an immediate armistice; to be followed by a peace conference. In April of this year, Germany herself proposed peace. The peace movements are strong in England, France and United States; and in Germany. In the Reichstag, the peace groups are active and outspoken; the exact terms of Germany's offer have never been made known to us and I should like to ask Lloyd George what his war aims are.

The politicians chatter like imbeciles while civilisation bleeds to death. Consider the plight of the civilised world after another year of war: you do not know what you do, and the statesmen wash their hands of the whole affair. We are killing off slowly but surely the best of the male population on the barbed wire, because you, the misguided masses, are crying out for it.

Patricia Beer

The Night Marlowe Died

Christopher Marlowe was a spy, it seems.
His day of pleasure by the River Thames
Should have brought him a handshake and a watch
For faithful service. He had done as much
For anyone who paid him and so had
His three companions. They were really good.

In those days spying was expertly done.
Informers took each other's washing in.
Double agents cancelled themselves out.
Spying had paid for all the wine and meat
Which filled the little room that day in spring
When Marlowe met a different reckoning.

He had been his usual snorting, railing
Blasphemous self, but loyal to his calling,
As they all had to be, to live so well.
He sang a noisy song before he fell,
A dagger stuck in his eye after the feast
As though the Cross had got to him at last.

They saw each other home after his death.
The rats had tired, the streets were out of breath.
Somewhere asleep, the top spymasters lay
Unpicking webs that they had spun by day.
Somewhere, across a park, a peacock's cries
Bewailed the pointlessness of murdering spies.

Elizabeth Jennings

The Rabbit's Advice

I have been away too long.
Some of you think I am only a nursery tale,
One of which you've grown out of.
Or perhaps you saw a movie and laughed at my ears
But rather envied my carrot.
I must tell you that I exist.

I'm a puff of wool leaping across a field,
Quick to all noises,
Smelling my burrow of safety.
I am easily frightened. A bird
Is tame compared to me.
Perhaps you have seen my fat white cousin who sits,
Constantly twitching his nose,
Behind bars in a hutch at the end of a garden.
If not, imagine those nights when you lie awake
Afraid to turn over, afraid
Of night and dawn and sleep.
Terror is what I am made
Of partly, partly of speed.

But I am a figure of fun.
I have no dignity
Which means I am never free.
So, when you are frightened or being teased, think of
My twitching whiskers, my absurd white puff of a tail,
Of all that I mean by 'me'
And my ludicrous craving for love.

Seamus Heaney

Blackberry-Picking

For Philip Hobsbaum

Late August, given heavy rain and sun
For a full week, the blackberries would ripen.
At first, just one, a glossy purple clot
Among others, red, green, hard as a knot.
You ate that first one and its flesh was sweet
Like thickened wine: summer's blood was in it
Leaving stains upon the tongue and lust for
Picking. Then red ones inked up and that hunger
Sent us out with milk-cans, pea-tins, jam-pots
Where briars scratched and wet grass bleached
   our boots.
Round hayfields, cornfields and potato-drills
We trekked and picked until the cans were full,
Until the tinkling bottom had been covered
With green ones, and on top big dark blobs burned
Like a plate of eyes. Our hands were peppered
With thorn pricks, our palms sticky as Bluebeard's.

We hoarded the fresh berries in the byre.
But when the bath was filled we found a fur,
A rat-grey fungus, glutting on our cache.
The juice was stinking too. Once off the bush
The fruit fermented, the sweet flesh would turn sour.
I always felt like crying. It wasn't fair
That all the lovely canfuls smelt of rot.
Each year I hoped they'd keep, knew they would not.

Roger McGough
Just Another Autumn Day

> In Parliament, the Minister for Mists
> and Mellow Fruitfulness announces,
> that owing to inflation and rising costs
> there will be no Autumn next year.
> September, October and November
> are to be cancelled,
> and the Government to bring in
> the nine-month year instead.
> Thus will we all live longer.
>
> Emergency measures are to be introduced
> to combat outbreaks of well-being
> and feelings of elation inspired by the season.
> Breathtaking sunsets will be restricted
> to alternate Fridays, and gentle dusks
> prohibited. Fallen leaves will be outlawed,
> and persons found in possession of conkers,
> imprisoned without trial.
> Thus will we all work harder.
>
> The announcement caused little reaction.
> People either way don't really care
> No time have they to stand and stare
> Looking for work or slaving away
> Just another Autumn day.

Peter Bland

Gargoyle in a Country Churchyard

Ugly alright; hunch-backed, squat-thighed,
eyes bulging backwards into the worn

church wall that mothers him. And
working still – snouting rainspill

down from the guttering
on to the dead below. How well

the day-labourers buried here – these
forgotten Quasimodos of the fields –

would have seen in this hunched beast
a caricature of themselves. Gargoyles

are born to labour, to curse and spit. Angels
ape the gentry and wear pleated shifts.

Leonard Clark

Singing in the Streets

I had almost forgotten the singing in the streets,
Snow piled up by the houses, drifting
Underneath the door into the warm room,
Firelight, lamplight, the little lame cat
Dreaming in soft sleep on the hearth, mother dozing,
Waiting for Christmas to come, the boys and me
Trudging over blanket fields waving lanterns to the sky.
I had almost forgotten the smell, the feel of it all,
The coming back home, with girls laughing like stars,
Their cheeks, holly berries, me kissing one,
Silent-tongued, soberly, by the long church wall;
Then back to the kitchen table, supper on the
    white cloth,
Cheese, bread, the home-made wine,

Symbols of the night's joys, a holy feast.
And I wonder now, years gone, mother gone,
The boys and girls scattered, drifted away with the
    snowflakes,
Lamplight done, firelight over,
If the sounds of our singing in the streets are still there,
Those old tunes, still praising;
And now, a lifetime of Decembers away from it all,
A branch of remembering holly stabs my cheeks,
    And I think it may be so;
    Yes, I believe it may be so.

Thomas Hardy
The Going

Why did you give me no hint that night
That quickly after the morrow's dawn,
And calmly, as if indifferent quite,
You would close your term here, up and be gone
    Where I could not follow
    With wing of swallow
To gain one glimpse of you ever anon!

    Never to bid good-bye,
    Or lip me the softest call,
Or utter a wish for a word, while I
Saw morning harden upon the wall,
    Unmoved, unknowing
    That your great going
Had place that moment, and altered all.

Why do you make me leave the house
And think for a breath it is you I see
At the end of the alley of bending boughs
Where so often at dusk you used to be;
    Till in darkening dankness

The yawning blankness
Of the perspective sickens me!

You were she who abode
By those red-veined rocks far West,
You were the swan-necked one who rode
Along the beetling Beeny Crest,
And, reining nigh me,
Would muse and eye me,
While life unrolled us its very best.

Why, then, latterly did we not speak,
Did we not think of those days long dead,
And ere your vanishing strive to seek
That time's renewal? We might have said,
'In this bright spring weather
We'll visit together
Those places that once we visited.'

Well, well! All's past amend,
Unchangeable. It must go.
I seem but a dead man held on end
To sink down soon... O you could not know
That such swift fleeing
No soul foreseeing –
Not even I – would undo me so!

B R Whiting
Individualist

Splitting firewood I often found
Fat white grubs in the grain
And would toss them on the ground –
The fowls learned this, and a vain
Old crow who posed apart in liberty
Used to wait for me to throw

The juicy ones under his special tree,
Where he would stab them straight
Before the frantic fowls arrived –
Bird-brain, they were in such a state,
The brown contentious crowd that lived
In a clucking strain of imitation.
But then, a cackling hen, meanly
By cunning, running to look
Would try to beat the mob to it again,
Push up, put her head on the block,
Staring, arrogant, stupid, plain,
And I would cut it off, throw
It to the black and elegant crow
Who did not rely on my offering –
There was no change in the fowlyard cries,
They were indifferent to headless suffering,
And he would peck out its beady eyes.

Henrik Ibsen (Adapted by the compilers)
from **The Wild Duck** *(Act Three)*

Hedvig ...No, I don't go to school anymore; father's afraid of me hurting my eyes. He has promised to read with me; but he hasn't had time yet. I spend a good deal of time in the attic. It's like a world of its own and there are such lots of wonderful things. There are big cupboards full of books, and a great many of the books have pictures in them, and there's a big bureau with drawers and flaps, and a big clock with figures that come out. But it doesn't go now. And there's an old paint-box and things of that sort. Most of the books are English, though, and I don't understand English. But then I look at the pictures. There's one great big book called 'Harryson's History of London'. It must be a hundred years old; and there are such heaps of pictures in it. At the beginning there's Death with an hour-glass, and a girl. I think that's horrid. But then there are all the other pictures of churches, and castles, and streets, and big ships sailing on the sea...

An old sea captain once lived here, and he brought them home. They used to call him the 'The Flying Dutchman'. That was curious because he wasn't a Dutchman. But he disappeared at last; and so he left all these things behind him… I mean always to stay at home and help father and mother… I should love above everything to learn to engrave pictures like those in the English books. I don't think father likes it; he's so strange about that. Only think, he talks of my learning basket-weaving and straw-plaiting! But I don't think *that* would lead to much. But father was right in saying that if I learnt basket-making I could have made the new basket for the wild duck… It's MY wild duck, it belongs to me. But I lend it to father and grandfather as often as they please. They look after it, and build places for it, and so on… She's a real wild fowl, you know. And she's so much to be pitied; she has no one to care for her, poor thing… The hens were chickens together; but she's been taken right away from all her belongings. And then there's such a lot that's strange about the wild duck. Nobody knows her, and nobody knows where she came from either.

Sebastian Barry
from ***The Steward of Christendom*** *(Act One)*

Dolly I was down at the North Wall with the Galligan sisters.

Maud At the North Wall?

Annie What were you doing there, Dolly?

Dolly Mary Galligan was going out with one of the Tommies, and he and his troop were heading off home today, so we went down to see them off.

Annie *(sorting socks)* Well, well, I don't know, Dolly, if you aren't the biggest fool in Christendom.

Dolly No, I'm no fool. They were nice lads. There was a good crowd down there, and the Tommies were in high spirits, singing and so on. It was very joyful.

Maud You've to keep your skirts long these times, Dolly. You're not to be seen waving to soldiers.

Dolly They're going from Ireland and they'll never be back, why shouldn't we say goodbye? Do you know every barracks in Ireland has lost its officers and men? Regiments that protected us in the war, who went out and left thousands behind in France. Willie's own regiment is to be disbanded, and that's almost entirely Dublin lads.

Annie Dolly, why are you so surprised? Haven't we known for the last six months that Ireland is to be destroyed? I don't know why it's such news to you. Haven't you listened? Haven't you seen your father's face? Haven't you felt for him, Dolly?

Dolly It's different when you see it.

Annie You're a fool, Dolly.

Dolly I'm no fool.

(Annie picks up in one hand the good socks and in the other the ones needing mending – they look like two woolly hands themselves)

And I'll tell you. Coming home in the tram, up the docks road, Mary Galligan was crying, and we were talking kindly to her, and trying to comfort her, and I don't know what we said exactly, but this woman, a middle-aged woman, quite well-to-do, she rises up and stands beside us like a long streak of misery, staring at us. And she struck Mary Galligan on the cheek, so as she left the marks of her hand there. And she would have attacked me too, but that the conductor came down and spoke to the woman. And she said we were Jezebels and should have our heads shaved and be whipped for following the Tommies. And the conductor looked at her, and hadn't he served in France himself, as one of the Volunteers, oh, it was painful, the way she looked back at him, as if he were a viper or a traitor. The depth of foolishness in her. A man that had risked himself, like Willie, but that had reached home at last.

(Dolly crying)

Christopher Fry

from **The Boy With a Cart**

> **Cuthman** I was alone by the unattended pillar,
> Mourning the bereaved air that lay so quiet
> Between walls; hungry for hammer-blows
> And the momentous hive that once was there.
> And when I prayed my voice slid to the ground
> Like a crushed pediment.
> There was demolition written over
> The walls, and dogs rummaged in the foundations,
> And picnic parties laughed on a heap of stone.
> But gradually I was aware of some one in
> The doorway and turned my eyes that way and saw
> Carved out of the sunlight a man who stood
> Watching me, so still that there was not
> Other such stillness anywhere on the earth,
> So still that the air seemed to leap
> At his side. He came towards me, and the sun
> Flooded its banks and flowed across the shadow.
> He asked me why I stood alone. His voice
> Hovered on memory with open wings
> And drew itself up from a chine of silence
> As though it had longtime lain in a vein of gold.
> I told him : It is the king-post.
> He stretched his hand upon it. At his touch
> It lifted to its place. There was no sound.
> I cried out, and I cried at last 'Who are you?'
> I heard him say 'I was a carpenter'…
> There under the bare walls of our labour
> Death and life were knotted in one strength
> Indivisible as root and sky.

Grade 6

Michael Drayton
Sonnet

Since ther's no helpe, Come let us kisse and part,
Nay, I have done: You get no more of Me,
And I am glad, yea glad with all my heart,
That thus so cleanly, I my Selfe can free,
Shake hands for ever, Cancell all our Vowes,
And when We meet at any time againe,
Be it not seene in either of our Browes,
That We one jot of former Love reteyne;
Now at the last gaspe, of Love's latest Breath,
When his Pulse fayling, Passion speechlesse lies,
When Faith is kneeling by his bed of Death,
And Innocence is closing up his Eyes,
    Now if thou would'st, when all have given him over,
    From Death to Life, thou might'st him yet recover.

Siegfried Sassoon
Ancient History

Adam, a brown old vulture in the rain,
Shivered below his wind-whipped olive-trees;
Huddling sharp chin on scarred and scraggy knees,
He moaned and mumbled to his darkening brain;
'He was the grandest of them all – was Cain!
'A lion laired in the hills, that none could tire;
'Swift as a stag; a stallion of the plain,
'Hungry and fierce with deeds of huge desire.'

Grimly he thought of Abel, soft and fair –
A lover with disaster in his face,
And scarlet blossom twisted in bright hair.
'Afraid to fight; was murder more disgrace?…
'God always hated Cain'… He bowed his head –
The gaunt wild man whose lovely sons were dead.

William Shakespeare

Sonnet 87

> Farewell thou art too dear for my possessing,
> And like enough thou know'st thy estimate,
> The charter of thy worth gives thee releasing:
> My bonds in thee are all determinate.
> For how do I hold thee but by thy granting,
> And for that riches where is my deserving?
> The cause of this fair gift in me is wanting,
> And so my patent back again is swerving.
> Thyself thou gav'st, thy own worth then not knowing,
> Or me to whom thou gav'st it, else mistaking,
> So thy great gift upon misprision growing,
> Comes home again, on better judgment making.
> > Thus have I had thee as a dream doth flatter,
> > In sleep a king, but waking no such matter.

John Keats

When I have fears that I may cease to be

> When I have fears that I may cease to be
> > Before my pen has gleaned my teeming brain,
> Before high-piled books, in charact'ry
> > Hold like rich garners the full ripened grain;
> When I behold, upon the night's starred face,
> > Huge cloudy symbols of a high romance,
> And think that I may never live to trace
> > Their shadows, with the magic hand of chance;
> And when I feel, fair creature of an hour!
> > That I shall never look upon thee more,
> Never have relish in the faery power
> > Of unreflecting love! – then on the shore
> Of the wide world I stand alone, and think
> Till Love and Fame to nothingness do sink.

e e cummings
i thank you God

> i thank You God for most this amazing
> day: for the leaping greenly spirits of trees
> and a blue true dream of sky; and for everything
> which is natural which is infinite which is yes
>
> (i who have died am alive again today,
> and this is the sun's birthday; this is the birth
> day of life and of love and wings; and of the gay
> great happening illimitably earth)
>
> how should tasting touching hearing seeing
> breathing any – lifted from the no
> of all nothing – human merely being
> doubt unimaginable You?
>
> (now the ears of my ears awake and
> now the eyes of my eyes are opened)

Gerard Manley Hopkins
Spring

> Nothing is so beautiful as Spring –
>> When weeds, in wheels, shoot long and lovely and lush;
>> Thrush's eggs look little low heavens, and thrush
> Through the echoing timber does so rinse and wring
> The ear, it strikes like lightnings to hear him sing;
>> The glassy peartree leaves and blooms, they brush
>> The descending blue; that blue is all in a rush
> With richness; the racing lambs too have fair their fling.
>
> What is all this juice and all this joy?
>> A strain of the earth's sweet being in the beginning
>> In Eden garden. – Have, get, before it cloy,
>
>> Before it cloud, Christ, lord, and sour with sinning,
> Innocent mind and Mayday in girl and boy,
>> Most, O maid's child, thy choice and worthy the winning.

Thomas Hood

Silence

There is a silence where hath been no sound,
      There is a silence where no sound may be,
      In the cold grave – under the deep, deep sea,
Or in wide desert where no life is found,
Which hath been mute, and still must sleep profound;
      No voice is hush'd – no life treads silently,
      But clouds and cloudy shadows wander free,
That never spoke, over the idle ground:
But in green ruins, in the desolate walls
      Of antique palaces, where Man hath been,
Though the dun fox or wild hyaena calls,
      And owls that flit continually between,
Shriek to the echo, and the low winds moan –
There the true Silence is, self-conscious and alone.

Gwen Harwood

Suburban Sonnet

She practises a fugue, though it can matter
to no one now if she plays well or not.
Beside her on the floor two children chatter,
then scream and fight. She hushes them. A pot
boils over. As she rushes to the stove
too late, a wave of nausea overpowers
subject and counter-subject. Zest and love
drain out with soapy water as she scours
the crusted milk. Her veins ache. Once she played
for Rubinstein, who yawned. The children caper
round a sprung mousetrap where a mouse lies dead.
When the soft corpse won't move they seem afraid.
She comforts them; and wraps it in a paper
featuring: *Tasty dishes from stale bread.*

———

Brian Clark

from **Whose Life is it Anyway?** *(Act Two)*

Ken That's a disturbing tidiness compulsion you've got there.

Travers I was an only child. Have you any relationships outside the hospital? You're not married, I see.

Ken No, thank God.

Travers A girlfriend?

Ken A fiancée, actually. I asked her not to visit me any more. About a fortnight ago.

Travers She must have been upset.

Ken Better that, than a lifetime's sacrifice.

Travers She wanted to – stay with you, then.

Ken Oh yes – had it all worked out. But she's a young, healthy woman. She wants babies – real ones. Not ones that never *will* learn to walk.

Travers But if that's what she really wants.

Ken Oh come on, Doctor. If that's what she really wants, there's plenty of other cripples who want help. I told her to go to release her, I hope, from the guilt she would feel if she did what she really wanted to.

Travers That's very generous.

Ken Balls. Really, Doctor, I did it for *me*. It would destroy *my* self respect if I allowed myself to become the object with which people can safely exploit their masochist tendencies.

Travers That's putting it very strongly.

Ken Yes. Too strong. But you are beginning to sound like the chaplain. He was in here the other day. He seemed to think I should be quite happy to be God's chosen vessel into which people could pour their compassion – that it was all right being a cripple because it made other folk feel good when they helped me.

Travers What about your parents?

Ken Working-class folk – they live in Scotland. I thought it would break my mother – I always thought of my father as a very tough egg. But it was the other way round. My father can only think with his hands. He used to stand around here – completely at a loss. My mother would sit there – just understanding. She knows what

suffering's about. They were here a week ago – I got rid of my father
for a while and told my mother what I was going to do. She looked at
me for a minute. There were tears in her eyes. She said 'Aye lad, it's thy
life – don't worry about your dad – I'll get him over it… She stood up
and I said: 'What about you?' 'What about me?' she said, 'Do you think
life's so precious to me, I'm frightened of dying?' I'd like to think I was
my mother's son.

    Travers *(after a pause)* Yes well, we shall have to see…

    Ken What about, you mean you haven't made up your mind?

    Travers I shall have to do some tests…

    Ken What tests, for Christ's sake? I can tell you now, my time over
a hundred metres is lousy.

    Travers You seem very angry.

    Ken Of course I'm angry. No, no – I'm… yes. I am angry.
(Breathing) But I am trying to hold it in because you'll just write me
off as in a manic phase of a manic depressive cycle.

    Travers You are very free with psychiatric jargon.

    Ken *(breathing)* Oh well then, you'll be able to say I'm an
obsessive hypochondriac.

    Travers I certainly wouldn't do that, Mr Harrison.

    Ken Can't you see what a trap I am in. Can anyone prove that they
are sane? Could you?

    Travers I'll come and see you again.

    Ken No, don't come and see me again, because every time you
come I get more and more angry, and more and more upset and
depressed. And eventually, you will destroy my mind.

Stella Gibbons (Adapted by Paul Doust)

from Cold Comfort Farm *(Act One, Scene One)*

(Neck enters)

> **Neck** Hey, Charlie baby… !
>
> **Flora** *(to the audience)* Mr Neck.
>
> **Neck** I've been out in that bi-plane nearly… Oh, now wait a minute! Wait a minute! Gee, but this'd make some location! Boy, *what* a location! I've got to come back here sometime – when I've found myself my new actor! Flora sweetheart – speak to your folks here for me will you? Tell 'em a big Hollywood producer wants to shoot a picture. Tell 'em I'll pay anything! Anything! Hey, that's it! I'll send 'em on a vacation of a lifetime! The South of France! The hotel *I'm* staying at, OK? *(He produces a brochure and hands it to Flora)* The Hotel Miramar! See? Just look at the life they lead out there! All those dames just lying around in the sun? You put an old bird on the side of that pool – and she feels a million years younger. Oh yes! I seen it happen! I tell you babes, there's only one place in this whole world near half as beautiful as the Hotel Miramar – and that's right here in Sussex. Hautcouture Hall! I met the family on this Search of a Star, stuff. I was looking for someone English, you know, but earthy. So I fixed to test the kid – Dick. Richard Hawk-Monitor. But it didn't work out. Not that he wasn't a dish! Oh, boy – what a dish! But he was too damned… *British.* See? British Reserve. And British Reserve is *not* what they want. Not anymore. No – what they want now is *Passion!* I want a fella who can take that screen in the palm of his hand and have the dames just melt right through the floor! A big, husky stiff! Red blood! I need a guy who looks great in a tuxedo – but even better half out of it! Know what I mean? Hence – I gotta go to France! Well I've looked every other place! And if I don't find him soon, I'm sunk! So – come on now, Charlie! Wake up! Smell the coffee! I've *hired* you and your wings to fly me over there, haven't I? Let's fly! Know what I mean? So long, toots – see you again!

(Neck exits)

David Hare

from Skylight *(Act Two, Scene One)*

Kyra Tom, I'm just asking, but are you developing just a bit of a chip?

Tom Not at all.

(Bad-temperedly he moves to get himself more scotch, but nothing will stop her now.)

Kyra I mean, like earlier… earlier this evening, you were going on about 'business'. 'No-one understands *business*,' that's what you said. Suddenly, I must say, I hear it everywhere. These so-called achievers telling us they have a grievance. The whole of society must get down on their knees and thank them, because they do something they no longer call 'making money'. Now we must call it something much nicer. Now we must call it 'the creation of wealth'…

(Tom looks at her uneasily, but she is really enjoying herself)

Putting money in your pocket. No longer the happy matter of just piling up coins. Oh no. We all have to say it's an intrinsically worthy activity. And the rest of us, we're ungrateful… we're immoral… we must simply be *envious*… if we don't constantly say so out loud. You have to laugh. It's this modern phenomenon. Suddenly this new disease! Self-pity! Self-pity of the rich! No longer do they simply accumulate. Now they want people to line up and thank them as well. *(She moves towards him, more serious now.)* Well, I tell you, I spend my time among very different people. People who often have nothing at all. And I find in them one great virtue at least: unlike the rich, they have no illusions that they must once have done something right! Nor do they suffer from delicate feelings. They don't sit about whining. How misunderstood and undervalued they are. No, they're getting on with the day-to-day struggle of trying to survive on the street. And that street, I tell you… if you get out there… if you actually have to learn to survive, well, it's a thousand times harder than leading an export drive, being in government, or, yes, I have to say, it's even harder than running a bank. *(She nods at this gentle reference to what he said earlier. She is quieter now)* And the sad thing, Tom, is that you once knew that. When I first met you, you knew that full well. It marked you. That was the charm of you. It made you different. And I'm not sure the moment at which you forgot.

David Mamet

from Oleanna (Act Two)

Carol How can you *deny* it. You did it to me. *Here*. You *did…* You *confess*. You love the Power. To *deviate*. To *invent*, to transgress… to *transgress* whatever norms have been established for us. And you think it's charming to 'question' in yourself this taste to mock and destroy. But you should question it. Professor. And you pick those things which you feel *advance* you: publication, *tenure*, and the steps to get them you call 'harmless rituals.' And you perform those steps. Although you say it is hypocrisy. But to the aspirations of your students. Of *hardworking students*, who come here, who *slave* to come here – you have no idea what it cost me to come to this school – you *mock* us. You call education 'hazing' and from your so-protected, so-elitist seat you hold our confusion as a *joke*, and our hopes and efforts with it. Then you sit there and say 'what have I done?' And ask me to understand that *you* have aspirations too. But I tell you. I tell you. That you are vile. And that you are exploitative. And if you possess one ounce of that inner honesty you describe in your book, you can look in yourself and see those things that I see. And you can find revulsion equal to my own. Good day. *(She prepares to leave the room.)*

Githa Sowerby

from *Rutherford & Son* *(Act Three)*

Mary You can listen – then you can take it or leave it.

Rutherford Thank ye kindly. And what's your idea of a bargain?

Mary A bargain is where one person has something to sell that another wants to buy. There's no love in it – only money – money that pays for life. I've got something to sell that you want to buy.

Rutherford What's that?

Mary My son. *(Their eyes meet in a long steady look. She goes on deliberately)* You've lost everything you have in the world. John's gone – and Richard – and Janet. They won't come back. You're alone now and getting old, with no one to come after you. When you die Rutherford's will be sold – somebody'll buy it and give it a new name perhaps, and no one will even remember that you made it. That'll be the end of all your work. Just – nothing. You've thought of that. I've seen you thinking of it as I've sat by and watched you. And now it's come… Will you listen?

Rutherford Ay.

(She sits down at the other end of the table, facing him)

Mary It's for my boy. I want – a chance of life for him – his place in the world. John can't give him that, because he's made so. If I went to London and worked my hardest I'd get twenty-five shillings a week. We've failed. From you I can get what I want for my boy. I want – all the good common things: a good house, good food, warmth. He's a delicate little thing now, but he'll grow strong like other children. I want to undo the wrong we've done him, John and I. If I can. Later on there'll be his schooling – I could never save enough for that. You can give me all this – you've got the power… That's the bargain. Give me what I ask, and in return I'll give you – him. On one condition. I'm to stay on here. I won't trouble you – you needn't speak to me or see me unless you want to. For ten years he's to be absolutely mine, to do what I like with. You mustn't interfere – you mustn't tell him to do things or frighten him. He's mine. For ten years more.

Thornton Wilder

from Our Town (Act One)

Stage Manager I think this is a good time to tell you that the Cartwright interests have just begun building a new bank in Grover's Corners – had to go to Vermont for the marble, sorry to say. And they've asked a friend of mine what they should put in the cornerstone for people to dig up... a thousand years from now... Of course, they've put in a copy of the *New York Times* and a copy of Mr Webb's *Sentinel*... We're kind of interested in this because some scientific fellas have found a way of painting all that reading matter with a glue – a silicate glue – that'll make it keep a thousand – two thousand years.

We're putting in a Bible... and the Constitution of the United States – and a copy of William Shakespeare's plays. What do you say, folks? What do you think?

Y'know – Babylon once had two million people in it, and all we know about 'em is the names of the kings and some copies of wheat contracts... and contracts for the sale of slaves. Yet every night all those families sat down to supper, and the father came home from his work, and the smoke went up the chimney – same as here. And even in Greece and Rome, all we know about the *real* life of the people is what we can piece together out of the joking poems and the comedies they wrote for the theatre back then.

So I'm going to have a copy of this play put in the cornerstone and the people a thousand years from now'll know a few simple facts about us – more than the Treaty of Versailles and the Lindbergh flight.

See what I mean?

So – people a thousand years from now – this is the way we were in the provinces north of New York at the beginning of the twentieth century – This is the way we were: in our growing up and in our marrying and in our living and in our dying.

W H Auden

The Unknown Citizen

To JS/07/M/378

This Marble Monument is Erected by the State

He was found by the Bureau of Statistics to be
One against whom there was no official complaint,
And all the reports on his conduct agree
That, in the modern sense of an old-fashioned word,
he was a saint,
For in everything he did he served the Greater Community.
Except for the War till the day he retired
He worked in a factory and never got fired,
But satisfied his employers, Fudge Motors Inc.
Yet he wasn't a scab or odd in his views,
For his Union reports that he paid his dues,
(Our report on his Union shows it was sound)
And our Social Psychology workers found
That he was popular with his mates and liked a drink.
The Press are convinced that he bought a paper every day
And that his reactions to advertisements were normal in
every way.
Policies taken out in his name prove that he was fully
insured,
And his Health-card shows he was once in hospital but left
it cured.
Both Producers Research and High-Grade Living declare
He was fully sensible to the advantages of the Instalment
Plan
And had everything necessary to the Modern Man,
A phonograph, a radio, a car and a frigidaire.
Our researchers into Public Opinion are content
That he held the proper opinions for the time of year;

When there was peace, he was for peace; when there was
war, he went.

He was married and added five children to the population,

Which our Eugenist says was the right number for a parent
of his generation,

And our teachers report that he never interfered with their
education.

Was he free? Was he happy? The question is absurd:

Had anything been wrong, we should certainly have heard.

Kahil Gibran

Love (from The Prophet)

Then said Almitra, Speak to us of Love.

And he raised his head and looked upon the people, and there fell a
stillness upon them. And with a great voice he said:

When love beckons to you, follow him,

Though his ways are hard and steep.

And when his wings enfold you yield to him,

Though the sword hidden among his pinions

may wound you.

And when he speaks to you believe in him,

Though his voice may shatter your dreams as

the north wind lays waste the garden.

For even as love crowns you so shall he crucify you. Even as he is
for your growth so is he for your pruning.

Even as he ascends to your height and caresses your tenderest
branches that quiver in the sun,

So shall he descend to your roots and shake them in their clinging
to the earth.

Like sheaves of corn he gathers you unto himself.

He threshes you to make you naked.

He sifts you to free you from your husks.

He grinds you to whiteness.

He kneads you until you are pliant;

And then he assigns you to his sacred fire, that you may become sacred bread for God's sacred feast.

All these things shall love do unto you that you may know the secrets of your heart, and in that knowledge become a fragment of Life's heart.

J B Priestley (Adapted by the compilers)
from An Inspector Calls (Act Two)

Gerald All right, if you *must* know. I met her first, sometime in March last year, in the stalls bar at the Palace. I mean the Palace music hall in Brumley.

I happened to look in, one night, after a rather long dull day, and as the show wasn't very bright, I went down into the bar for a drink. It's a favourite haunt of women of the town. I didn't propose to stay long down there. I hate those hard-eyed dough-faced women. But then I noticed a girl who looked quite different. She looked young and fresh and charming and altogether out of place down there. And obviously she wasn't enjoying herself. Old Joe Meggarty, half-drunk and goggle-eyed, had wedged her into a corner with that obscene fat carcase of his. The girl saw me looking at her and then gave me a glance that was nothing less than a cry for help. So I went across and told Joe Meggarty some nonsense – that the manager had a message for him or something like that – got him out of the way and then told the girl that if she didn't want any more of that sort of thing, she'd better let me take her out of there.

We went along to the County Hotel, which I knew would be quiet at that time of night, and we had a drink or two and talked. She told me her name was Daisy Renton, that she'd lost both parents, that she came originally from somewhere outside Brumley. She also told me she'd had a job in one of the works here and had had to leave after a strike. She said something about the shop too, but wouldn't say which it was, and she was deliberately vague about what happened. I couldn't get any exact details from her about her past life. She wanted to talk about herself – just because she felt I was interested and friendly – but at the same time she wanted to be Daisy Renton – and not Eva Smith. In fact, I heard that name for the first time tonight. What she did let slip – though she didn't mean to – was that she was desperately hard up and at that moment was actually hungry. I made the people at the County find some food for her.

(Steadily) I discovered, not that night but two nights later, when we met again – not accidentally this time of course – that in fact she hadn't a penny and was going to be turned out of the miserable back room she had. It happened that a friend of mine, Charlie Brunswick, had gone off to Canada for six months and had let me have the key of a nice little set of rooms he had – in Morgan Terrace – and had asked me to keep an eye on them for him and use them if I wanted to. So I insisted on Daisy moving into those rooms and I made her take some money to keep her going there.

(Carefully to the Inspector) I want you to understand that I didn't install her there so that I could make love to her. I made her go to Morgan Terrace because I was sorry for her, and didn't like the idea of her going back to the Palace bar. I didn't ask for anything in return.

Howard Brenton (Adapted by the compilers)
from **The Churchill Play** *(Act Three)*

Caroline Mummy will give us money for the house, Julian. Julian? Say yes. It's not actually in Maidstone. More on the outskirts of Maidstone. Julian, Mummy's put a deposit down. Don't be angry. Don't be hurt. Don't be upset. Don't go cold on me. *(bitterly)* I don't know why you have to feel so guilty. You do feel guilty. Because you're in the Army and because you're a doctor. In a prison camp. Guilt. It drips off you. Like a runny nose... For Godsake... You don't have to stay here... I look out of the window. The window of our married quarters. At the rain. And the mud. And the huts. And the men, going from hut to hut, on the duckboards. This morning I saw a man stumble. He stumbled off the boards, into the mud. It came up to his knee. Where does the mud come from? The ever-deepening mud. And when there is a fine day the men light fires. You look across the compounds… and the men are stooping, by little fires… I've never understood why they do that. What do they have to burn? It's not only to keep warm. At the height of summer there will be little fires, the men stooped over them. It seems for miles. The prison is so strange. Another thing, why do the men stuff the windows of the huts with rags? Nail the rags over the glass, where they can. I'm so frightened. So deeply frightened of this place. I want to go back down South. I want you out of the Army and a real doctor again. Worrying about little girls' tonsils and little boys' acne. Not crucifying yourself for being half doctor, half prison guard. Tearing yourself apart. Crying in your sleep. I'm frightened, I'm sick scared. Julian? Julian? *(He does not answer.)* You were going to do research. Heart diseases? You loved heart diseases. You'd talk for hours into the night, about heart diseases. Julian? Oh, I know that silence. *(Bitterly)* That stiff neck. Go on, go on… Flick your neck! Jerk your neck, like a little boy. *(A slight pause, he flicks his head)* That's it! The I am so innocent, sensitive and delicate gesture. *(Savagely)* The little flick *(pause)* Julian? *(No answer)* It's not bad, what I want, is it? It's no disgrace? A house with a garden, in the south of England. Decent. Mild. Safe. Away from this… Rural slum. Slum landscape, slum fen… Cabbage fields for miles. Derelict airfields… On the horizon, barbed wire… Men by little fires… *(Near tears)* Julian? *(Nothing from Thompson)* No disgrace. Not wanting to be the English wife. Of the English Doctor. Of an English concentration camp… That's what you are, my love.

Dylan Thomas (Adapted by the compilers)
from The Fight *(from Portrait of the Artist as a Young Dog)*

Boy I was standing at the end of the lower playground and annoying Mr Samuels, who lived in the house just below the high railings. Mr Samuels complained once a week that boys from the school threw apples and stones and balls through his bedroom window. He sat in a deck-chair in a small square of trim garden and tried to read the newspaper. I was only a few yards from him. I was staring him out. He pretended not to notice me, but I knew he knew I was standing there rudely and quietly. Every now and then he peeped at me from behind his newspaper, saw me still and serious and alone, with my eyes on his. As soon as he lost his temper I was going to go home. Already I was late for dinner. I had almost beaten him, the newspaper was trembling, he was breathing heavily, when a strange boy, whom I had not heard approach, pushed me down the bank.

I threw a stone at his face. He took off his spectacles, put them in his coat pocket, took off his coat, hung it neatly on the railings, and attacked. Turning round as we wrestled on the top of the bank, I saw that Mr Samuels had folded his newspaper on the deck-chair and was standing up to watch us. It was a mistake to turn round. The strange boy rabbit-punched me twice. Mr Samuels hopped with excitement as I fell against the railings. I was down in the dust, hot and scratched and biting, then up and dancing, and I butted the boy in the belly and we tumbled in a heap. I saw through a closing eye that his nose was bleeding. I hit his nose. He tore at my collar and spun me round by the hair. Mr Samuels started shouting 'Come on! Come on!'

We both turned towards him. He was shaking his fists and dodging about in the garden. He stopped then, and coughed, and set his panama straight, and avoided our eyes, and turned his back and walked slowly to the deck chair.

Philip Larkin

An Arundel Tomb

Side by side, their faces blurred,
The earl and countess lie in stone,
Their proper habits vaguely shown
As jointed armour, stiffened pleat,
And that faint hint of the absurd –
The little dogs under their feet.

Such plainness of the pre-baroque
Hardly involves the eye, until
It meets his left-hand gauntlet, still
Clasped empty in the other; and
One sees, with a sharp tender shock,
His hand withdrawn, holding her hand.

They would not think to lie so long.
Such faithfulness in effigy
Was just a detail friends would see:
A sculptor's sweet commissioned grace
Thrown off in helping to prolong
The Latin names around the base.

They would not guess how early in
Their supine stationary voyage
The air would change to soundless damage,
Turn the old tenantry away;
How soon succeeding eyes begin
To look, not read. Rigidly they

Persisted, linked, through lengths and breadths
Of time. Snow fell, undated. Light
Each summer thronged the grass. A bright
Litter of birdcalls strewed the same
Bone-riddled ground. And up the paths
The endless altered people came,

Washing at their identity.
Now, helpless in the hollow of
An unarmorial age, a trough
Of smoke in slow suspended skeins
Above their scrap of history,
Only their attitude remains.

Time has transfigured them into
Untruth. The stone fidelity
They hardly meant has come to be
Their final blazon, and to prove
Our almost-instinct almost true:
What will survive of us is love.

Ted Hughes
The Jaguar

The apes yawn and adore their fleas in the sun.
The parrots shriek as if they were on fire, or strut
Like cheap tarts to attract the stroller with the nut.
Fatigued with indolence, tiger and lion

Lie still as the sun. The boa-constrictor's coil
Is a fossil. Cage after cage seems empty, or
Stinks of sleepers from the breathing straw.
It might be painted on the nursery wall.

But who runs like the rest past these arrives
At a cage where the crowd stands, stares, mesmerized,
As a child at a dream, at a jaguar hurrying enraged
Through prison darkness after the drills of his eyes

On a short fierce fuse. Not in boredom –
The eye satisfied to be blind in fire,
By the bang of blood in the brain deaf the ear –
He spins from the bars, but there's no cage to him

More than to the visionary his cell:
His stride is wildernesses of freedom:
The world rolls under the long thrust of his heel.
Over the cage floor the horizons come.

Eavan Boland
Moths

Tonight the air smells of cut grass.
Apples rust on the branches. Already summer is
a place mislaid between expectation and memory.

This has been a summer of moths.
Their moment of truth comes well after dark.
Then they reveal themselves at our window-
ledges and sills as a pinpoint. A glimmer.

The books I look up about them are full of legends:
ghost-swift moths with their dancing assemblies at dusk.
Their courtship swarms. How some kinds may steer by the
    moon.

The moon is up. The back windows are wide open.
Mid-July light fills the neighbourhood. I stand by the hedge.

Once again they are near the windowsill –
fluttering past the fuchsia and the lavender,
which is knee-high, and too blue to warn them

they will fall down without knowing how
or why what they steered by became, suddenly,
what they crackled and burned around. They will perish –

I am perishing – the edge and at the threshold of
the moment all nature fears and tends towards:

the stealing of the light. Ingenious facsimile.

And the kitchen bulb which beckons them makes
my child's shadow longer than my own.

Siegfried Sassoon
Falling Asleep

> Voices moving about in the quiet house;
> Thud of feet and a muffled shutting of doors;
> Everyone yawning. Only the clocks are alert.
> Out in the night there's autumn-smelling gloom
> Crowded with whispering trees, across the park
> A hollow cry of hounds like lonely bells;
> And I know that the clouds are moving across the moon;
> The low, red, rising moon. Now herons call
> And wrangle by their pool; and hooting owls
> Sail from the wood above pale stooks of oats.
>
> Waiting for sleep, I drift from thoughts like these;
> And where to-day was dream-like, build my dreams.
> Music… there was a bright white room below,
> And someone singing a song about a soldier,
> One hour, two hours ago; and soon the song
> Will be 'last night'; but now the beauty swings
> Across my brain, ghost of remembered chords
> Which still can make such radiance in my dream
> That I can watch the marching of my soldiers,
> And count their faces; faces, sunlit faces.
> Falling asleep… the herons, and the hounds…
> September in the darkness; and the world
> I've known; all fading past me into peace.

Thomas Hardy
from The Woodlanders *(Chapter 47)*

The moon, that had imperceptibly added her rays to the scene, shone almost vertically. It was an exceptionally soft, balmy evening for the time of year, which was just that transient period in the May month when beech trees have suddenly unfolded large limp young leaves of the softness of butterflies' wings. Boughs bearing such leaves hung low around and completely inclosed them, so that it was as if they were in a great green vase, which had moss for its bottom and leaf sides. Here they sat down.

The clouds having been packed in the west that evening so as to retain the departing glare a long while, the hour had seemed much earlier than it was. But suddenly the question of time occurred to her.

'I must go back,' she said, springing up; and without further delay they set their faces towards Hintock. As they walked he examined his watch by the aid of the now strong moonlight.

'By the gods, I think I have lost my train!' said Fitzpiers.

'Dear me – whereabouts are we?' said she.

'Two miles in the direction of Sherton.'

'Then do you hasten on, Edred. I am not in the least afraid. I recognize now the part of the wood we are in, and I can find my way back quite easily. I'll tell my father that we have made it up. I wish I had not kept our meetings so private, for it may vex him a little to know I have been seeing you. He is getting old and irritable, that was why I did not. Good-bye.'

'But, as I must stay at the Earl of Wessex to-night, for I cannot possibly catch the train, I think it would be safer for you to let me take care of you.'

'But what will my father think has become of me! He does not know in the least where I am – he thinks I only went into the garden for a few minutes.'

'He will surely guess – somebody has seen me for certain. I'll go all the way back with you to-morrow.'

'But that newly-done-up place – the Earl of Wessex!'

'If you are so very particular about the publicity I will stay at a little quiet one.'

'O no – it is not that I am particular – but I haven't a brush or comb or anything!'

Bertolt Brecht (Translated by Eric Bentley)
from The Good Woman of Setzuan (Scene Ten)

(The court is cleared. Silence.)

    Shui ta Illustrious ones!

    (The gods look at each other, not quite believing their ears)

    Shui ta Yes, I recognize you!

    Second god *(Taking matters in hand, sternly)* What have you done with our good woman of Setzuan?

    Shui ta I have a terrible confession to make: I am she! *(He takes off his mask, and tears away his clothes. Shen te stands there)*

    Second god Shen Te!

    Shen Te Shen Te, yes. Shui Ta *and* Shen Te. Both.

> Your injunction
> To be good and yet to live
> Was a thunderbolt:
> It has torn me in two
> I can't tell how it was
> But to be good to others
> And myself at the same time
> I could not do it
> Your world is not an easy one, illustrious ones!
> When we extend our hand to a beggar, he tears
>   it off for us
> When we help the lost, we are lost ourselves
> And so
> Since not to eat is to die
> Who can long refuse to be bad?
> As I lay prostrate beneath the weight of good
>   intentions
> Ruin stared me in the face
> It was when I was unjust that I ate good meat
> And hob-nobbed with the mighty
> Why?
> Why are bad deeds rewarded?

Good ones punished?

I enjoyed giving

I truly wished to be the Angel of the Slums

But washed by a foster-mother in the water of
    the gutter

I developed a sharp eye

The time came when pity was a thorn in my side

And, later, when kind words turned to ashes in
    my mouth

And anger took over

I became a wolf

Find me guilty, then, illustrious ones,

But know:

All that I have done I did

To help my neighbour

To love my lover

And keep my little one from want

For your great, godly deeds, I was too poor, too
    small.

Franz Kafka

The Burrow *(Adapted from The Metamorphosis and Other Stories)*

Narrator I have completed the construction of my burrow and it seems to be successful. All that can be seen from the outside is a big hole; that, however, really leads nowhere; if you take a few steps you strike against natural firm rock. I can make no boast of having contrived this ruse intentionally; it is simply the remains of one of my many abortive building attempts, but finally it seemed to me advisable to leave this one hole without filling it in. True, some ruses are so subtle that they defeat themselves, I know that better than anyone, and it is certainly a risk to draw attention by this hole to the fact that there may be something in the vicinity worth inquiring into. But you do not know me if you think I am afraid, or that I built my burrow simply out of fear. At a distance of some thousand paces from this hole lies, covered by a movable layer of moss, the real entrance to the burrow; it is secured as safely as anything in this world can be secured; yet someone could step on the moss or break through it, and then my burrow would lie open, and anybody who liked – please note, however, that quite uncommon abilities would also be required – could make his way in and utterly destroy everything. I know that very well, and even now when I am better off than ever before I can scarcely pass an hour in complete tranquility; at that one point in the dark moss I am vulnerable, and in my dreams I often see a greedy muzzle sniffing round it persistently. It will be objected that I could quite well have filled in the entrance too, with a thin layer of hard earth on top and with loose soil further down, so that it would not cost me much trouble to dig my way out again whenever I liked. But that plan is impossible; prudence itself demands that I should have a way of leaving at a moment's notice if necessary, prudence itself demands, as alas! so often, the element of risk in life.

John Barton and Kenneth Cavander

from **The Greeks** (Part Two)

>**Seris** It happened to me at midnight.
>I felt soft and sleepy:
>The feasting was over,
>The singing was done
>And we were tired from dancing.
>My husband lay on our bed,
>His spear hung on the wall.
>The plains of Troy were empty.
>For the first time in ten years
>There were no Greeks. They'd gone.
>I was letting down my hair,
>Combing it with my hands,
>And smiling in my mirror.
>I thought of making love.
>Then I heard a noise.

Someone shouted out,
'On Greeks, and sack the city.
Then we can all go home!'
I was… *at home*.
All that I had on
Was a thin dress, the sort
That the girls of Sparta wear.
I prayed. No one answered.
My turn came. They dragged me
Like everybody else
Down to the beach to the ships.
On the way I saw my husband
Lying dead in the street.

There is nothing I can do
Except to curse Helen
And Paris, her lover.
They did it… they did.

Chorus: May the winds blow
Against her forever.
– May she choke in the sea.
– May rocks gash her face.
– May nothing be left but carrion
For gulls to pick at.
– Helen, Helen, Helen.

Seris Helen, whore of Troy.

Alan Ayckbourn

from **Man of the Moment** *(Act Two)*

Later that same afternoon. At the start, as before, there is just a light on
Jill who sits on the patio doing a piece to camera. The film crew, as
always, are out of sight.

Jill It became increasingly clear the quiet, law-abiding,
undemanding Douglas Beechey we had met and spoken to in Purley a
few days before was a very different creature from the man who had
arrived here at the Parks' villa earlier that day. Here was a person who,
at last, seemed to have discovered a long-lost purpose. As each of his
senses, in turn, took in the unfamiliar – the sweet perfume of luxury,
the rich, clean vista of good living, the comfortable, self-confident
murmur of opulence – his manner grew ever more watchful –
increasingly thoughtful. Were these merely the signs of a man finally
coming to terms with his lot? A man at last accepting that most
unacceptable of truths – that life *is* unjust? Or was there a darker,
more dangerous emotion starting to emerge from this hitherto
undemonstrative man. Was this an anger, an envy, even a dim
forgotten desire for revenge… ? *(She pauses, dramatically)*

(As Jill has spoken the lights have slowly widened, as before)

Cut. *(She rises and talks to the crew)* That OK?

(A shouted reply)

Yes, thank you very much. I meant technically OK, Dan – I can do
without the editorial, thank you. Can we set up in the study now,
please? We'll just do Vic's interview, then that's it for today, all right?
(Waving them round.) Go through the front. Through the front door,
it'll be easier. I'll see you there.

(Jill gathers up her folder from the table. She flicks through it to find
her questions for Vic. Kenny wanders out with a drink in his hand)

Kenny *(Watching her)* Are you thinking of doing your interview
with Vic fairly soon?

Jill Yes. They're just setting it up…

Kenny You'd better get a move on. The rate he's pouring it down
himself, he won't be able to string two words together…

Jill God, I asked him to go easy –

Kenny Oh yes? I'll tell him you're nearly ready. In the study?

Jill I'll be right there. He is forty-seven, isn't he?

Kenny Forty-seven, yes. Forty-eight next May.

Jill *(Scribbling this on to her note)* Does he mind it being mentioned?

Kenny He never has done.

Jill If I get Vic done now, then tomorrow morning I can spend with Mr Beechey and that leaves me the rest of the day clear – till our flight, to do general shots of the island… Should be all right. Always providing I can get Mr Beechey to say anything remotely interesting…

Kenny He tries his best, I think.

Jill It was a complete waste of time just now with the three of us. It was all Vic talking. Beechey never said a word –

Kenny Well, Vic's an expert, isn't he? I mean, he's done hundreds of these things. How many's Douglas done?

Jill I gave him his chance. Douglas, what do *you* think? Douglas, what do *you* say to that? You heard me. Nothing. Not a usable syllable. *(Excitedly.)* I tell you, Kenny, somehow or other – if I'm going to make any sort of programme – I have got to find a way to prise that man open. Get to the heart of him. I know, you see, I know that under all that suburban – blandness – that dreary flock-wallpaper personality of his – there is a real person there. There is pain – there is disappointment – there is a burning resentment – hopefully even hatred, who knows.

Kenny Really? Are you sure?

Jill There has to be. Please God there is.

Kenny He seems pretty well-balanced to me.

Jill There has to be. Or the man wouldn't be human.

Sheila Yeger

from Self Portrait (Act One)

(Gwen moves away from her, agitated)

Gwen Shall we start? While there's still some light?

Dorelia Work. I almost forgot.

Gwen It's what we came for.

Dorelia Is it?

(Dorelia rather reluctantly takes up the pose Gwen stands at the easel and looks at Dorelia)

Gwen The hands are too low.

(Dorelia adjusts her hands. Gwen is still dissatisfied. She goes across to Dorelia and shifts her hands by a fraction of an inch then stands back and squints at her)

There's still something wrong.

(She adjusts the pose again and stands back)

Sorry… you must feel like a sack of coal.

Dorelia It's always like that when you model.

Gwen Even when you model for the great Augustus John?

Dorelia Especially.

(They laugh. Gwen begins to prepare her palette)

Gwen Sometimes I wonder… Will we ever be as good as the men? Those wonderful old masters… and the modern men too. At college I used to look at them all… so full of it always. They seem so enormous. Almost as if they might swell up and occupy the whole world… as if we'd better move fast before they take over everything and there's no space left for us and our little bits of work. The trouble is, the thought of it makes us hurry… *(looks up)* Can you open your eyes very slightly… ?

You look a bit too modest.

(Dorelia laughs and abandons the pose)

Please, Dodo… the light's going.

(Dorelia reorganises herself)

Dorelia Sorry… it was the thought of modesty.

(Gwen goes over and adjusts the bow on Dorelia's dress then returns to the easel. A long pause)

Gwen Do you ever think of Ida? How she feels?

Dorelia Ida doesn't mind about me. Not one little bit. Anyway, artists aren't like normal people… she must have known that when she married Gus. Gus says every great artist has either starved in a garret or had a string of mistresses… sometimes both… it'll all part of the mystique, he says.

Gwen You're talking rubbish as usual. Dangerous rubbish at that. Anyway… none of that interests me in the slightest. Work. That's the only thing. If the men want to play at being artists, let them. But if we women want to be taken seriously, we have to regard ourselves with the utmost seriousness.

(*Dorelia yawns hugely then laughs*)

Dorelia Sorry

(*Gwen puts down her brush*)

Gwen Evidently you find this all a little tedious.

Dorelia I thought art would be fun.

Gwen Then you thought wrong. Stand still, for God's sake.

(*Dorelia wanders over to look at the painting.*)

Dorelia You make me look really wanton.

(*Gwen looks at her, then back to the painting. Dorelia still stares at it, fascinated, then she coils up her hair with her hand, in a rather provocative gesture. Suddenly she snatches Gwen's paintbrush and sticks it in her hair, then she runs off, brandishing it, laughing wildly. Gwen runs after her, catches her, holds her. Both are laughing. Freeze. Then Dorelia runs off*)

Gwen Dodo… Dodo… don't leave, not yet. He took you away… But it was all my own doing… I told you to go… How could I hold you… ? It was like trying to hold a wild animal… like a part of myself I must always hold in check… in case… in case… (*Pause*) I wanted to get it right. All of it. I always wanted so badly to get it right.

Alan Ayckbourn

from *Confusions* *(Gosforth's Fête)*

Gosforth So far so good. *(He climbs onto the platform. He taps the mike experimentally)* One – two – three – four – success. Good afternoon to you, ladies and gentlemen – boys and girls. *(Breaking off as he sights something)* Will you Wolf Cubs not persecute that pig, please. Now keep well clear of the pig – thank you. *(Resuming)* May I first of all thank you all for braving the elements this afternoon and coming along here to support this very worthwhile cause. That cause is, as we all know, the building of the new village hall. Something that eventually can be enjoyed by each and everyone of us in this community. I won't keep you longer than I have to – I'm well aware this is hardly the weather for standing about and listening to speeches. We will, in view of the circumstances, be altering our programme of events slightly. We plan to take tea in the tea tent, that is the tent from which I am speaking to you now, immediately after we have heard from our distinguished Guest of Honour. She herself needs very little introduction I am sure. Both she and her husband have both served as councillors for this ward for many years and during that time have, I feel – and here I'm speaking over and above any purely party political feeling – have, I feel done tremendous work both for us and for that whole community to which we all belong. Without further ado, may I call upon Councillor Mrs Pearce formally to open this Grand Fête. Councillor Mrs Pearce.

W B Yeats

The Second Coming

> Turning and turing in the widening gyre
> The falcon cannot hear the falconer;
> Things fall apart; the centre cannot hold;
> Mere anarchy is loosed upon the world,
> The blood-dimmed tide is loosed, and everywhere
> The ceremony of innocence is drowned;
> The best lack all conviction, while the worst
> Are full of passionate intensity.
>
> Surely some revelation is at hand;
> Surely the Second Coming is at hand.
> The Second Coming! Hardly are those words out
> When a vast image out of *Spiritus Mundi*
> Troubles my sight: somewhere in sands of the desert
> A shape with a lion body and the head of a man,
> A gaze blank and pitiless as the sun,
> Is moving its slow thighs, while all about it
> Reel shadows of the indignant desert birds.
> The darkness drops again; but now I know
> That twenty centuries of stony sleep
> Were vexed to nightmare by a rocking cradle,
> And what rough beast, its hour come round at last,
> Slouches toward Bethlehem to be born?

Harry Guest

Brutus in His Orchard

> Lull in the storm. Between these walls
> a sense of time mislaid.
> No moon.
> The constellations blurred by cloud.

The trees hang heavy in the dark.
An owl's note shivers from the distance.
Drenched grass. Spread cobwebs here and there
catch at the glimmer of a falling star.

The hours drift to a standstill.
Night. And somewhere. Does the way
lie in this direction,
that or this? And dawn's
grey knifeblade at the east
behind which branch leafless, invisible?

Meteors pierce the mist,
leave red tracks on the sky.
The cold air apprehensive
and the compass gone.

Far thunder.
    Still
the time seems ripe. And death
at this extinguished moment
logical, not to be feared.
A step toward oblivion.
No more.

I am not I. And nowhere. Am
a process of thought
lost in the darkness, dark mind
without position, past or action.

Inside the night. And by myself.
What I must do is harm. Now.
Either way.

A light.
The boy approaches.
Perhaps a message or reprieve.
The wind gets up once more, some rain
spills on my hand and I'm
no longer quite alone.

Leonard Clark

Charles

He was born blind with the snow on a winter's day;
The moon blank as marble stared at him from the full,
But his mother wept to see the vacant rolling of his eyes;
His father dared not look and despairingly turned away
When hands like feelers fumbled in space to pull
Fingers and lips to upturned face to recognize.
Growing older he sat in the dark learning voices by heart,
Carried on conversations with birds singing in summer trees,
Heard brooks changing their sound at floodtime, the
    angled dart
Of dazzled bats diving through twilight air.
But music played by wandering band or organ at the fair
Moved him to tears and fingers to invisible keys,
So that at twenty-five he began to drown the village church
With ceaseless tides of Handel, Bach and Mendelssohn,
And magnified the Lord for seven-and-thirty years.
With egg-shaped head he sat upright upon his perch,
Praying on flute we might depart in peace,
Triumphant came from Egypt on the bombardon,
Made thunderstorms at will, stars race like charioteers,
Captivity to turn, the harvest to increase;
He brought sweet healing to the troubled mind,
Fearlessly opened the eyes of the blind.

C Day Lewis
The Album

I see you, a child
In a garden sheltered for buds and playtime,
Listening as if beguiled
By a fancy beyond your years and the flowering maytime.
The print is faded: soon there will be
No trace of that pose enthralling,
Nor visible echo of my voice distantly calling
'Wait! Wait for me!'

Then I turn the page
To a girl who stands like a questioning iris
By the waterside, at an age
That asks every mirror to tell what the heart's desire is.
The answer she finds in that oracle stream
Only time could affirm or disprove,
Yet I wish I was there to venture a warning, 'Love
Is not what you dream.'

Next you appear
As if garlands of wild felicity crowned you –
Courted, caressed, you wear
Like immortelles the lovers and friends around you.
'They will not last you, rain or shine,
They are but straws and shadows,'
I cry: 'Give not to those charming desperadoes
What was made to be mine.'

One picture is missing –
The last. It would show me a tree stripped bare
By intemperate gales, her amazing
Noonday of blossom spoilt which promised so fair.
Yet, scanning those scenes at your heyday taken,
I tremble, as one who must view

In the crystal a doom he could never deflect – yes, I too
Am fruitlessly shaken.

I close the book;
But the past slides out of its leaves to haunt me
And it seems, wherever I look,
Phantoms of irreclaimable happiness taunt me.
Then I see her, petalled in new-blown hours,
Beside me – 'All you love most there
Has blossomed again,' she murmurs, 'all that you missed there
Has grown to be yours.'

D H Lawrence

from *Odour of Chrysanthemums* *(A short story)*

Miners, single, trailing, and in groups, passed like shadows diverging
home. At the edge of the ribbed level of sidings squat a low cottage,
three steps down from the cinder track. A large bony vine clutched at
the house, as if to claw down the tiled roof. Round the bricked yard
grew a few wintry primroses. Beyond, the long garden sloped down to
a bush-covered brook course. There were some twiggy apple trees,
winter-crack trees, and ragged cabbages. Beside the path hung
dishevelled pink chrysanthemums, like pink cloths hung on bushes. A
woman came stooping out of the felt-covered fowl-house, half-way
down the garden. She closed and padlocked the door, then drew
herself erect, having brushed some bits from her white apron.

She was a tall woman of imperious mien, handsome, with definite
black eyebrows. Her smooth black hair was parted exactly. For a few
moments she stood steadily watching the miners as they passed along
the railway: then she turned, towards the brook course. Her face was
calm and set, her mouth was closed with disillusionment. After a
moment she called:

'John!' There was no answer. She waited, and then said distinctly:
'Where are you?'

'Here!' replied a child's sulky voice from among the bushes. The woman looked piercingly through the dusk.

'Are you at that brook?' she asked sternly.

For answer the child showed himself before the raspberry-canes that rose like whips. He was a small, sturdy boy of five. He stood quite still, defiantly.

'Oh!' said that mother, conciliated. 'I thought you were down at that wet brook – and you remember what I told you –'

The boy did not move or answer.

'Come, come on in,' she said more gently, 'it's getting dark. There's your grandfather's engine coming down the line!'

Rabindranath Tagore

A Poet's School (from *This World is Beautiful*)

In my school, I myself have never taught anything but languages and literature. I cannot produce any certificates for you but I can assure you that I taught them well. My pupils have told me they have never had a better language teacher. It goes without saying that I love words. A word for me is as living as a flower or a butterfly. Each word has its lustre, its sparkle, its subtle charm. That helped me to teach well all the languages that I know. I have had that experience with one pupil, my wife, whom I taught English in six months. An inspector of the University of Calcutta came to see me one day. He had seen me reading with my twelve-year-old boys Shelley's 'Hymn to Intellectual Beauty' and he was surprised to see me reading with these children a text which is included in the curriculum of colleges and universities. Nevertheless, I do not believe in being able to make things childish in order to give them to children. I respect children and they understand me. It must be said also that I have been remarkably well supported. At the beginning of my school, a young poet of nineteen had voluntarily come forward to offer me his collaboration. If he had not died at the age of twenty, today he would have been one of the great poets of the world. He read Browning with his little pupils in a manner that made them feel the beauty of his poems. One can only teach what one loves. If one does not love what one teaches, one had better be silent. Also, you must teach only what has an element of mystery for you.

I have said this to my mathematician friends. They will be able to teach the multiplication table well only if they love it. There are undoubtedly some who have a love for it. For me, it is inscribed in the petals of flowers and in the veins of leaves. Without knowing it, the butterflies carry it on their wings. I have said this to my friends, the mathematics teachers, and offered to share their teaching. They have shrugged their shoulders and dismissed my ideas as madness. It is probably because they are not poets just as I am not a mathematician. Nevertheless, I am convinced that one teaches best whatever has a touch of poetry for him.

Sam Shepard

from Fool for Love

The Old Man *(to Eddie)* Boy, is she ever off the wall with this one. You gotta' do somethin' about this.

May The funny thing was, that almost as soon as we'd found him – he disappeared. She was only with him about two weeks before he just vanished. Nobody saw him after that. Ever. And my mother – just turned herself inside out. I never could understand that. I kept watching her grieve, as though somebody'd died. She'd pull herself up into a ball and just stare at the floor. And I couldn't understand that because I was feeling the exact opposite feeling. I was in love, see. I'd come home after school, after being with Eddie, and I was filled with this joy and there she'd be – standing in the middle of the kitchen staring at the sink. Her eyes looked like a funeral. And I didn't know what to say. I didn't even feel sorry for her. All I could think of was him.

The Old Man *(to Eddie)* She's gettin' way outa' line here.

May And all he could think of was me. Isn't that right, Eddie. We couldn't take a breath without thinking of each other. We couldn't eat if we weren't together. We couldn't sleep. We got sick at night when we were apart. Violently sick. And my mother even took me to see a doctor. And Eddie's mother took him to see the same doctor but the doctor had no idea what was wrong with us. He thought it was the flu or something. And Eddie's mother had no idea what was wrong with him. But my mother – my mother knew exactly what was wrong. She knew it clear down to her bones. She recognized every symptom. And she begged me not to see him but I wouldn't listen. Then she begged Eddie not to see me but he wouldn't listen. Then she went to Eddie's mother and begged her. And Eddie's mother – *(Pause. She looks straight at Eddie)* – Eddie's mother blew her brains out. Didn't she, Eddie? Blew her brains right out.

David Edgar

from Destiny *(Act Two, Scene Eight)*

Lights. Rolfe stands. He is in a dark overcoat, over a suit which shows signs of hasty travel. The stage is empty, though we are in fact in the Army HQ Lisburn, Northern Ireland. Rolfe holds a union jack, crumpled in this hands. He almost cradles it, as he would a baby. He looks up at the audience.

Rolfe There is a moment in one's life, more terrible, traumatic, even than the ending of a first love, or the consciousness of failed ambition, or awareness of the fact of growing old. It is the moment when you realise you have more time, regard, respect, for those who are your enemies than those you view as friends. That moment came to me at night, while sitting in an aeroplane, and flying northwards, west, across the Irish Sea, to fetch the body of my son.

He was, they told me, on the Lower Falls. Arms raid, just turned his head, a second. And the little boy, the school kid at the tenth floor window, with his sniper's gun, aimed just above the hairline, dead on true. Probably been there for hours. Waiting for that second. Patiently.

And on the plane, I realised, I had more time for him, the 12-year-old boy killer in the Divis Flats, the dark child with his Russian rifle, far more time for him, than they. The Generals. The Ministers. Assured

us that the sun would never set. The Generals, could not prevent my
son, in his high morning, his sun going down.

Yet you still won't see.

Will you? You generals, you ministers, police-chiefs, you won't see,
we are at war. Same war. In Belfast. Bradford. Bristol. Birmingham,
the one we lost in Bombay thirty years ago, the one we're going to lose
in Britain now. Unless you see in time.

Not thugs or lunatics, nor dupes of Moscow. They are ordinary
men and woman, sane and normal, thousands of them. And there is
no time. They're everywhere. Deep, deep, inside the gut. There is no
time.

(He is crying)

The sun has set. And we should not remember. We should not
look back, but should, instead, think only of the morning.

(He looks at the crumpled flag)

His fault. He turned his back

(The tears stop. Rolfe raises the flag, holding it in a high salute.)

We need an iron dawn.

(He stands there, holding up the flag. Lights fade to darkness.)

Anton Chekhov (Adapted by Michael Frayn)
from *Wild Honey* *(Act One, Scene Two)*

Osip I kissed her once.

Sasha Anna Petrovna? You kissed her? *(She sits beside him)*

Osip Hot summer's day. Like today. In the forest here. I'm going
along this track and I look round and there she is, she's standing in a
little stream and she's holding her dress up with one hand and she's
scooping up water in a dock leaf with the other. She scoops. She
drinks. Scoops. Drinks. Scoops again, and pours it over her head. It's
one of those days when you can feel the air heavy on you, and you
can't hear nothing but the buzzing of the flies… She pays no heed to
me. Just another peasant, she thinks. So I go down to the edge of the
stream, right close up to her, as close as I am to you now, and I just
look at her. Like this, like I'm looking at you. And she stands there in

the water in front of me, with her skirts up in her hand, and she bends, she scoops, she pours. And the water runs over her hair, over her face and her neck, then down over her dress, and all she says is: 'What are you staring at, idiot? Haven't you ever seen a human being before?' And she scoops and she pours, and I just stand gazing. Then suddenly she turns and gives me a sharp look. 'Oh,' she says, 'you've taken a fancy to me, have you?' And I say: 'I reckon I could kiss you and die.' So that made her laugh. 'All right,' she says, 'you can kiss me if you like.' Well, I felt as if I'd been thrown into a furnace. I went up to her – into the stream, boots and all, I didn't think twice – and I took her by the shoulder, very lightly, and I kissed her right here on her cheek, and here on her neck, as hard as ever I could.

Sasha So what did she do then?

Osip 'Now, then,' she says, 'be off with you! And you wash a little more often,' she says, 'and you do something about your nails!' And off I went.

Sasha She's a bold one, all right.

Osip After that you'd have thought I'd gone mad. Couldn't eat. Couldn't sleep. Everywhere I went I could see her in front of me. Shut my eyes – there she was again. I must have looked right soft. I wanted to go round and shoot the poor old general! And then she was widowed I started doing all kinds of little things for her. Shot partridges for her – caught quails – painted that old summerhouse of hers all different colours. Took her a live wolf once. She'd only to say and I'd have done it. Told me to eat myself and I'd have eaten myself… Took her a baby hare last year. She holds it in her arms, and she strokes it, and she says to me, 'Is it true what they say about you, Osip – that you're a bandit?' 'As true as I'm standing here,' I tell her. 'Then we're going to have to reform you,' she says. 'You'll have to go off on a pilgrimage. All the way to Kiev on foot. Then on to Moscow, and a year from now you'll be a different man.' Well, I got myself up like a beggar, I slung my bag on my back, and off I went to Kiev. Wasn't no use, though. Hadn't got no further than Kharkov when I fell in with a whole company of pilgrims. And what did I do? I drank my money, got in a fight, lost my papers, and came home again. Now she won't let me do nothing for her.

Brian Friel

from Faith Healer (Part One)

Frank Hardly ever cities or towns because the halls were far too dear for us. Seldom England because Teddy and Gracie were English and they believed, God help them, that the Celtic temperament was more receptive to us. And never Ireland because of me –

I beg your pardon – *The Fantastic Francis Hardy, Faith Healer, One Night Only. (A slight bow.)* The man on the tatty banner. *(He takes off his overcoat, selects an end chair from one of the rows, and throws the coat across it.)*

When we started out – oh, years and years ago – we used to have *Francis Hardy, Seventh Son of a Seventh Son* across the top. But it made the poster too expensive and Teddy persuaded me to settle for the modest 'fantastic'. It was a favourite word of his and maybe in this case he employed it with accuracy. As for the Seventh Son – that was a lie. I was in fact the only child of elderly parents, Jack and Mary Hardy, born in the village of Kilmeedy in County Limerick where my father was sergeant of the guards. But that's another story…

The initials were convenient, weren't they? FH – Faith Healer. Or if you were a believer in fate, you might say my life was determined the day I was christened. Perhaps if my name had been Charles Potter I would have been… Cardinal Primate; or Patsy Muldoon, the Fantastic Prime Minister. No, I don't mock those names. By no means. I'm not respectful but I don't mock.

Faith Healer – faith healing. A craft without an apprenticeship, a ministry without responsibility, a vocation without a ministry. How did I get involved? As a young man I chanced to flirt with it and it possessed me. No, no, no, no, no – that's rhetoric. No; let's say I did it… because I could do it. That's accurate enough. And occasionally it worked – oh, yes, occasionally it *did* work. Oh, yes. And when it did, when I stood before a man and placed my hands on him and watched him become whole in my presence, those were nights of exultation, of consummation – no, not that I was doing good, giving relief, but because the questions that undermined my life then became meaningless and because I knew that for those few hours I had become whole in myself, and perfect in myself, and in a manner of speaking, an aristocrat, if the term doesn't offend you.

Olwen Wymark
from Find Me

Jean What are we going to do? Dear God, what are we going to do? Managing! Perhaps it would be better for all of us if we couldn't manage. Then they'd have to do something. Maybe if I became an alcoholic… I could. My God, I think I could sometimes. *(Pause)* When I go next door to Suzanne's some nights and we sit and get a bit tight together on the whisky and talk about all sorts of things and laugh – just for a little while I can forget. The thoughts stop going round and round in my head. The relief of just feeling like an ordinary person. The relief. Supposing when Miss Everitt Social Services came round today she'd found me dead drunk on the floor. 'Dear me, Mrs Taylor, you're not managing wonderfully well today.' *(Pause)* Imagine your own child driving you to drink. Your own child that you love. *(Pause)* I don't know if I do love her. I don't know what I feel. Pity – oh, pity for her. Why did it have to happen? Poor Verity. Poor, poor baby. *(Pause)* But fear too. She seems to like to frighten me – enjoys it. She never does it to Edward. I really think sometimes she hates me. And he's so good to her – so patient and kind. All those holidays he takes her on. He doesn't talk about them afterwards but I know, I know she crucifies him. And I feel mean and cowardly because I don't go too. *(Pause)* And guilty. Did I do it? Was it my fault? When I was pregnant with her – all those weeks when she was inside me I thought she was so safe. Nothing could hurt her and yet all the time… was it me? Did I – contaminate her? Oh God… *(She stops herself)* She was so beautiful when she was a baby. Even now sometimes when you look at her when she's asleep. When I'm out with her sometimes I wish she was ugly. Deformed or crippled. Something people could *see*. Then they would pity her too. Instead of getting nervous and embarrassed and moving away from us as if we were lepers.

Oh God, will nobody help us?

Can't anybody help us?

David Hare

from The Secret Rapture *(Act Two, Scene Six)*

Isobel Well, no, I don't think so, I mean, look, I'm not complaining,
whatever's happened is my own fault, I was out of my depth, no, I was
weak, but putting that aside I have just been – what is the word for it?
– I think I have just been *asset-stripped.* Isn't that the term for it?
'Objectively', as you would say, I have just been trashed and spat out
in lumps. And now Tom has a corrugated hut at the back of his factory
between, as I saw it, the car park and the waste-disposal unit on the
industrial estate in Welwyn Garden City. *(She turns to Tom.)* Forgive
me, but I think even Jesus might have doubts about setting up a
business in there.

*(Surprisingly Tom chuckles at this, but Isobel's energy has unleashed
all Marion's incoherent fury)*

Marion Now this is it…

Isobel I'm sorry…

Marion This is exactly it. You spoil everything you touch.
Everywhere you go there are arguments. God, how I hate all this
human stuff. Wherever you go, you cause misery. People crying,
people not talking. It overwhelms me. Because you can't just live. Why
can't you *live* like other people? *(She stares at Isobel, distressed, in
tears)* Irwin came in here. He's in agony. He's a nice man.

Isobel I know Irwin's a nice man. He is a nice man. Except to me.
That's the difference. He's in the grip of an obsession. Which he can't
help. He's furious because I'm no longer in love with him. He can't
accept that. And because I know him very well, I'm fearful. Because
in a way I think he never will.

Marion Don't be ridiculous. He's just an ordinary person. We
talked to him. He's an ordinary man.

(Isobel turns, ignoring this)

Isobel And so I decided, perhaps it's irrational, all my life I've got
on with everyone. But this one time, all my instincts say, 'Do
something decisive. Cut him off. Wake him up. Shock him. Make it
final.' *(She turns, thoughtful now)* 'Do what needs to be done.'

Marion Really?

Isobel Yes.

Marion Was flying off necessary?

(Isobel smiles at the memory)

Tom Where did you go?

Isobel I took the first plane that came. Lanzarote, as it happened.

Tom How was that?

Isobel Paradise. I took all my clothes off and walked along the beach. Lanzarote was paradise. But unfortunately no use to me. *(She laughs.)* You can't get away. You think you can. You think you'll fly out. Just leave. Damn the lot of you, and go. Then you think, here I am, stark naked, sky-blue sea, miles of sand – I've done it! I'm free! Then you think, yes, just remind me, what am I meant to do now? *(She stands, a mile away in a world of her own)* In my case there's only one answer. *(She looks absently at them, as if they were not even present)* I must do what Dad would have wished. *(She turns, as if this were self-evident)* That's it.

Adam Pernak

from **Killers** *(Act Two, Scene Two)*

(The silent tape continues to run. Jonathan speaks in a rhythm: a swift and steady pace which he maintains.)

Jonathan Here I am – right – and my life – it's going on, going smoothly, no problems – Happy; you're happy; there's prospects – no good prospects. So I settle back – I'm OK – I start to plan things – make it better – move out, move on – I need support – I have you – it's logical – So I'm planning – and I'm happy – and then the promotion – I'm happier still – And I know you will be – I think you will be –

Then the party – everyone there – the next step – and I'm happy – but I'm nervous – because you're there – You're not happy – I'm doubtful – but never mind – there's the future – so I wait –

Then I see you – alone – then I ask you –

Then you tell me. *(Pause)* That was it – so…

It was the party… And then… *(Pause)*

So I have prospects – I have a job – a car –

OK, I have prospects – a job – a car –

(He starts to panic)

I have prospects – a future – 'You have the finest future ahead
of you' –

They like me – I'm popular – They tell me

(He stands, moves restlessly, irritated)

You can move on – you must build – build – build – build –

So I'm building –

I hear 'Move' – so I move – and I work – I work hard – and I'm
pushing – to get on – get up – I'm going on – it's going great – I'm very
well liked – very popular – I can hardly believe it.

(Pause)

(Slower) I took you to one side and said, 'This is what I want for
us'. I said 'us', not 'me'; it was always 'us'. You agreed. We shook
hands and we kissed and said 'Partners'. I remember.

(Back in pace) So I work – I've got a job – I'm moving up – a bigger
job – I'm feeling happy – that's the thing – and I've got you – that's
the thing –

(Pause)

(Slower) The first time… I went home and cried. I was so happy. I
knew, one way or the other, that there was something final about you.
How could I not feel something like that when it was clear, and you
were so right?

'You can't trust a soul,' Dad said.

I loved you more than anything. I said blue for the kitchen, but
you said white.

David would wear his uniform, and your sister would catch the
flowers, and we'd get them dancing together. We'd be a four then.

*(He is smiling. He stops and looks about him, baffled, lost. Focus on
this for several seconds.)*

(Finally) Where do I go? I can't just stop. I've got to move. Got to
change – progress. Where's the catch?

Look at this – it's got to stop – I can't have it – it must stop – Is it
funny? Should I laugh now? Is it funny? Is it a laugh?
I don't get it –

I have a job – a car – I have prospects –

Where are you, then? What is it? – it's me – Why me? –

Veronica – it's got to stop now –

David – I've got a job –

(Loudly, impatiently) What's the problem? What do you want now?

I've got my prospects –

(Pause. He settles down. He sits down, slowly)

I just want to know what I'm supposed to do.

I don't get it.

Mum…

I'm lost.

(Black out)

Herman Melville (Adapted by the editor from the novel)
from Moby Dick (Chapter 123)

Starbuck *(murmuring)* He would have shot me once. Yes, there's the very musket that he pointed at me; let me touch it, lift it. Strange that I should be shaking so. Loaded? I must see. Aye, aye. That's not good. I'll hold the musket boldly while I think. I come to report a fair wind to him. But how fair? Fair for death and doom – that's fair for Moby Dick. It's a fair wind that's only fair for that accursed fish. The very tube he pointed at me! This one that I hold here. He would have killed me with the very thing I handle now. Aye, and he would gladly kill all his crew. In these perilous seas he gropes his way by mere dead reckoning of a log abounding in errors – and in this typhoon did he not swear that he would have no lightning-rods? Shall this crazed old man be tamely suffered to drag a whole ship's company down to doom with him? Yes, it would make him the wilful murderer of thirty men and more if this ship come to any deadly harm, and by my soul, I swear it will if Ahab has his way. If then, he were this instant – put aside – that crime would not be his. Is he muttering in his sleep? Yes, just there, in there, he's sleeping. Sleeping, aye, but still alive, and soon awake again. I can't withstand thee then old man. Reasoning and entreaty thou scornest. Flat obedience to thy own flat commands is all thou breathest. Say'st the men have vowed thy vow? Great God forbid! Is there no other way – no lawful way? Make him a prisoner to be taken home? What! Hope to wrest this old man's living power from his own living hands? Only a fool would try it. Say he were pinioned even; knotted all over with ropes and hawsers, chained down to ring-bolts on this cabin floor. He would be more hideous than a caged tiger, then. I could not endure the sight; could not fly his howlings – all comfort, all reason would leave me on this intolerable voyage. What, then, remains? I stand alone upon an open sea. Two oceans and a whole continent lie between me and law. Aye, aye, 'tis so. Is heaven a murderer when lightning strikes a would-be murderer in his bed, scorching sheets and skin together? And would I be a murderer, then, if…

(Slowly, stealthily he places the loaded musket against the door)

The Captain's hammock swings within. A touch and Starbuck may survive to hug his wife and child again. Oh Mary! Boy, boy, boy! But if I wake thee not to death old man who can tell to what unsounded deeps Starbuck's body this day may sink – and all the crew sink with me! Great God, where are Thou? Shall I, shall I?

(A long pause. The musket, still raised, shakes in his hands)

The wind has dropped and shifted, sir. The sails are reefed and set. She heads her course.

Bertolt Brecht (Translated by John Willett)
from **The Good Person of Szechwan** (Scene Seven)

Shen Teh (softly) Oh joy! A small being is coming to life in my body. There is nothing to see yet. But he is already there. The world awaits him in secret. In the cities they have heard the rumour: someone is coming now with whom we must reckon. (*She presents her small son to the audience*) An airman!

Salute a new conqueror
Of unknown mountains, inaccessible countries! One
Carrying letters from man to man
Across the wastes where no man yet has trod!

(She begins to walk up and down, leading her small son by the hand) Come my son, inspect your world. Here, that is a tree. Bow politely, greet him. *(She performs a bow)* There, now you know one another. Listen, that is the water-seller coming. A friend, shake hands with him. Don't be nervous. 'A glass of cool water for my son, please. It's a hot day.' *(She hands him the glass)* Ah, the policeman! I think we will avoid him. Perhaps we might collect one or two cherries over there, from rich old Mr Feh Pung's orchard. This is a moment not to be seen. Come, poor little bastard! You too like cherries! Soft, soft, my son! *(They walk cautiously, looking around them)* No, round this way, where the bushes will shield us. No, no going straight to the point in this case. *(He seems to be dragging away; she resists)* We've got to be sensible. *(Suddenly she gives in)* Very well, if you can't do it any other way… *(She lifts him up)* Can you reach the cherries? Shove them in your mouth, that's the best place for them. *(She eats one herself, which he puts into her mouth)* Tastes fine. O god, the police. This is where we run. *(They flee)* Here's the road. Now gently, walk slowly so we don't attract attention. As if nothing whatever had happened… *(She sings as she walks along with the child:)*

A plum off my tree
Bit a man on the knee
The man had a thirst
Got his own bite in first.

Index by Author

Index by Title

Sources and Acknowledgements

Allan Ahlberg, **Billy McBone** from 'The Puffin Book of Twentieth-Century Children's Verse' (Puffin)

John Arden & Margaretta D'Arcy, **The Business of Good Government** (Methuen/R.I.B. Library Reed Book Services)

WH Auden, **The Unknown Citizen** from 'Collected Poems', edited by Edward Mendelson (Faber and Faber Ltd)

Alan Ayckbourn, **Confusions** (Methuen/R.I.B. Library Reed Book Services)

Alan Ayckbourn, **Man of the Moment** (Faber and Faber Ltd)

George Barker, **They Call to One Another** from 'To Aylsham Fair' (Faber and Faber Ltd)

Sebastian Barry, **The Steward of Christendom** (Methuen/R.I.B. Reed Book Services)

John Barton, **The Greeks** (Heinemann)

Patricia Beer, **E.T. Phone Home** and **The Night Marlowe Died** from 'Friend of Heraclitus' (Carcanet Press Ltd)

Peter Bland, **A Cape Town Christ** and **Gargoyle in a Country Churchyard** from 'Stone Tents' (The London Magazine)

Eavan Boland, **Moths** from 'In a Time of Violence' (Carcanet Press Ltd)

Bertolt Brecht, **The Caucasian Chalk Circle** and **The Good Person of Szechwan** (Methuen/ R.I.B. Library Reed Book Services)

Bertolt Brecht, **The Good Woman of Setzuan** (Penguin Plays)

Howard Brenton, **The Churchill Play** (Methuen/R.I.B. Library Reed Book Services)

Charles Causley, **Spin Me a Web, Spider** from 'Early in the Morning' (Puffin) and **What has happened to Lulu?**, from 'Collected Poems' (Macmillan) reproduced by permission of David Higham Associates

Anton Chekhov, **Wild Honey** (Methuen/R.I.B. Library Reed Book Services)

Leonard Clark, **Charles** from 'A Puffin Sextet of Poets' also in 'English Morning and Other Poems' (Hutchinson, 1953) and **Singing in the Streets** from 'Singing in the Streets, Poems for Christmas' (Dobson Books, 1972) reproduced by permission of the Literary Executor of Leonard Clark

Brian Clark, **Whose Life is it Anyway?** (Samuel French) reproduced by permission of Judy Daish Associates

Susan Cooper, **Seaward** (Puffin)

Pie Corbett, **Wind Poem** from 'Another Fifth Poetry Book' (OUP) reproduced by courtesy of the author

e e cummings, **i thank you God** from 'Complete Poems 1936-1962' (MacGibbon and Kee/Western Printing Services Ltd)

Joyce Dunbar, **Stuff** from 'Mouse and Mole' (Transworld Publishers Ltd)

David Edgar, **Destiny** (Methuen/R.I.B. Reed Book Services)

Max Fatchen, **Hair**, **Sea Talk** from 'Another Fourth Poetry Book' and **Why is it?** from 'Another Third Poetry Book' (OUP) reprinted by courtesy of John Johnson Ltd (Authors' Agents)

Eric Finney, **Whoppers** from 'Another Third Poetry Book' (OUP) reproduced by courtesy of the author

Brian Friel, **Faith Healer** (Gallery Books) reproduced by permission of Faber and Faber Ltd

Christopher Fry, **The Boy with a Cart** (OUP)

Stella Gibbons, **Cold Comfort Farm**, adapted for stage by Paul Doust (Samuel French) Copyright © Stella Gibbons 1932, reproduced by permission of Curtis Brown, London, and The Agency

Kahil Gibran, **Love** from 'The Prophet' (Heinemann)

Barbara Giles, **Drought in the Mallee, 1940** from 'Two Centuries of Australian Poetry' (OUP, Melbourne, Australia, 1992)

Harry Guest, **Brutus in His Orchard** from 'Lost and Found. Poems 1975-1982' ,pub.1983 (Anvil Press Poetry)

Thomas Hardy, extract from **The Woodlanders** and **The Going** from 'Complete Poems' (Macmillan General Books)

David Hare, **Skylight** and **The Secret Rapture** (Faber and Faber Ltd)

Gwen Harwood, **Suburban Sonnet** from 'Gwen Harwood – Selected Poems' (Angus and Robertson Publishers, Melbourne, Australia, 1981)

Seamus Heaney, **Blackberry-Picking** from 'Death of a Naturalist' (Faber and Faber Ltd)

Theresa Heine, **The Lonely Dragon** from 'Another First Poetry Book' (OUP) reprinted by permission of the author

Phoebe Hesketh, **Ward F4** from 'The Leave Train, New and Selected Poems by Phoebe Hesketh' (Enitharmon Press) © Phoebe Hesketh, 1989

Russell Hoban, **Homework** from 'Egg Thoughts and other Frances Songs' (Faber and Faber Ltd) and **What the Wind Said** from 'The Pedalling Man' (Heinemann) reproduced by permission of David Higham Associates

Julie Holder, **Nothing**, from 'Another First Poetry Book' (OUP)

William Horwood, **The Willows in Winter** (HarperCollins Publishers Ltd)

Ted Hughes, **The Jaguar** from 'The Hawk in the Rain', **There Came a Day** from 'Season Songs', **Mushrooms on the Moon** from 'Moon-Whales', extract from **The Iron Man** and **How the Whale Became** from 'How the Whale Became and other stories for children' (Faber and Faber Ltd)

Elizabeth Jennings, **The Owl's Request** from 'Poets in Hand' and **The Rabbit's Advice** from The Puffin Book of Twentieth-Century Children's Verse' (Puffin) by permission of David Higham Associates

Franz Kafka, **The Burrow**, from 'The Metamorphosis and Other Stories' (Penguin Modern Classics)

Clive King, **Stig of the Dump** (Penguin Books)

Philip Larkin, **An Arundel Tomb** from 'The Whitsun Weddings' (Faber and Faber Ltd)

DH Lawrence, **An Odour of Chrysanthemums** from 'The Prussian Officer and Other Short Stories' (OUP)

Henry Lawson, **The Water-Lily** from 'Poetical Works of Henry Lawson' (Angus and Robertson Publishers, NSW, Australia, 1986)

C Day Lewis, **The Album**, from 'The Oxford Book of Twentieth Century Verse' (OUP)

Joan Littlewood, **Oh What a Lovely War** (Methuen) reproduced by permission of the Tessa Sayle Agency

Penelope Lively, **Nat and the Great Bath Climb** from 'A House Inside Out' (André Deutsch)

Wes Magee, **Four Pirates** from 'A Third Poetry Book' (OUP)

David Mamet, **Oleanna** (Methuen/R.I.B. Reed Book Services)

Roger McGough, **Just Another Autumn Day** from 'Holiday on Death Row' (Jonathan Cape, 1979) and **Three Rusty Nails** from 'In the Glassroom' (Jonathan Cape, 1976) reproduced by permission of the Peters Fraser & Dunlop Group Ltd

David McKee, **Not Now Bernard** (Andersen Press Ltd)

Peter Miller & Randall Lewton, **The Sweeney Todd Shock 'n' Roll Show** (Samuel French Ltd)

Michael Morpurgo & Shoo Rayner, **Martians at Mudpuddle Farm** (Young Lions/HarperCollins Publishers Ltd)

Brian Moses, **The Way is Open** from 'Another Fifth Poetry Book' (OUP) reproduced by kind permission of the author

Judith Nicholls, **The Dentist** and **Counting Sheep** reproduced by kind permission of the author

Judith Nicholls, **The Bookshop** from 'Dragonsfire and Other Poems' and **Stable Song** from 'Magic Mirror and Other Poems for Children' (Faber and Faber Ltd)

Leslie Norris, **A Tiger in the Zoo** from 'A Fourth Poetry Book' (OUP)

Alfred Noyes, **Daddy Fell into the Pond** in various collections (Puffin)

Brian Owen, **The Evil Eye of Gondôr** (Samuel French Ltd)

Brian Patten, **The Newcomer** and **The Frogologist** from 'Gargling with Jelly' (Penguin); reproduced by kind permission of Brian Patten

Adam Pernak, **Killers** (Samuel French) reprinted by permission of Casarotto Ramsay Ltd

JB Priestley, **An Inspector Calls** (Samuel French) reproduced by permission of the Peters Fraser & Dunlop Group Ltd on behalf of the Estate

Jack Prelutsky, **Today is Very Boring** from 'The Puffin Book of Twentieth-Century Children's Verse' (Puffin)

Siegfried Sassoon, **Falling Asleep** and **Ancient History** (Faber and Faber Ltd) reproduced by kind permission of George Sassoon

Vernon Scannell, **Death of a Snowman** from 'The Apple Raid' (Chatto & Windus) reproduced by courtesy of the author

Catherine Sefton, **The Ghost and Bertie Boggin** (Puffin)

Sam Shepard, **Fool for Love** (Faber and Faber Ltd)

Shel Silverstein, **The Silver Fish** from 'A Third Poetry Book' (OUP)

Githa Sowerby, **Rutherford & Son** from 'New Woman Plays' (Methuen/R.I.B. Library Reed Book Services)

Robert Louis Stevenson, **Windy Nights** from 'Poems' (Penguin Books)

Rabindranath Tagore, **A Poet's School** from 'This World is Beautiful' (The Tagore Centre UK)

Dylan Thomas, **Under Milk Wood** and **The Fight** from 'Portrait of the Artist as a Young Dog' (JM Dent) reprinted by permission of David Higham Associates

JRR Tolkien, **The Hobbit** (HarperCollins Publishers Ltd)

Arnold Wesker, **The Kitchen** (Penguin Plays) reproduced by kind permission of the author

BR Whiting, **Individualist** from 'Two Centuries of Australian Poetry" (OUP, Melbourne, Australia, 1992)

Thornton Wilder, **Our Town** (Penguin Plays)

Raymond Wilson, **This Letter's to Say** from 'Another Fourth Poetry Book' (OUP)

David Wood, **The Pied Piper** (Samuel French) reproduced by kind permission of Casarotto Ramsay Ltd

Judith Wright, **The Trap** from 'Journeys' edited by Fay Zwicky (Sisters Publishing Ltd, Carlton, Victoria 3053, Australia, 1982) © Kit Wright, 1984

Kit Wright, **Granny Tom** from 'Cat Among the Pigeons' (Puffin) © Kit Wright

Olwen Wymark, **Find Me** (Samuel French) Reproduced by permission of The Agency (London) Ltd from FIND ME copyright © Olwen Wymark 1980, published by Samuel French. All rights reserved and any enquiries to The Agency (London) Ltd 24 Pottery Lane, London W11 4LZ Fax:0171 727 9037

WB Yeats, **The Second Coming** (Pan Macmillan) reproduced by permission of AP Watt Ltd

Sheila Yeger, **Self Portrait** reproduced by permission of Amber Lane Press Ltd, © Sheila Yeger, 1990